Inky Foot

Award-winning entries from the 1991
W H Smith Young Writers' Competition

M

MACMILLAN CHILDREN'S BOOKS

First published 1992 by
PAN MACMILLAN CHILDREN'S BOOKS
A division of Pan Macmillan Limited
Cavaye Place London SW10 9PG
and Basingstoke
Associated companies throughout the world

ISBN 0-333-57513-X

A CIP catalogue record for this book is available
from the British Library

Typeset by Macmillan Production Limited
Printed by Clays Limited, St Ives plc

Contents

Introduction

On a brilliantly hot day last July I presented the prizes at the Young Writers' Competition Awards Party at the National Theatre. Despite the heat, National Theatre actors Richard Hope and Griff Rhys Jones read out the prize winners' work with such infectious enthusiasm that it whetted our appetite for the book to come.

The book of winning stories and poems used to be called *Young Words*. This year, however, it is called *Inky Foot*, from the poem by Marcus Isaacs: like the penguin who signs a self-portrait with an inky foot, these young writers, too, have left their stamp on the work.

In 1939, on the death of W. B. Yeats, W. H. Auden wrote,

> Time that is intolerant
> Of the brave and innocent
> And indifferent in a week
> To a beautiful physique
>
> Worships language and forgives
> Everyone by whom it lives.

(from *In Memory of W. B. Yeats*)

This is the thirty-third Competition anthology. Many young writers whose work appeared in the first book are now in their forties, yet the youthful vision, fluency and freshness which caught the judges' eyes over thirty years ago lives on in their published words.

Everyone involved in the Competition lives by language. The young writers whose work appears here will live on through this book; and their teachers have shown them the power of language to persuade and entertain. Indeed, the competition survives and thrives through the hard work and dedication of teachers.

Parents, often forgotten in the excitement of prizes and publication, are responsible for introducing children to the excitement of language. The young writers in this book, and the hundreds who won commended certificates last year, could not have succeeded without families who foster a love of reading and who take a proud interest in their children's writing.

The Preliminary and Advisory Panels, led by Ted Hughes, deserve long-service medals. Many have worked on the Competition since it first started in 1959. They relish reading thousands of scripts from all over the United Kingdom. I understand their enthusiasm for fine writing but admire their stamina.

Of course, W H Smith should take a keen interest in those who live by language – the business depends on writers and journalists. The Young Writers' Competition is the centrepiece of the W H Smith Arts Programme which sponsors arts activities in schools. The Poetry Society's Poets in Schools Scheme and the Royal National Theatre's Interact are two such projects.

So, all of us who 'live by language' have a shared goal in spreading the word about the pleasures of reading and writing. *Inky Foot* continues an uninterrupted thirty-three-year journey to ensure that time remembers and honours language.

Sir Simon Hornby
Chairman of the W H Smith Group

Advisory panel of judges: Ted Hughes (Chairman), Michael Baldwin, Andrew Davies, Penelope Lively, Jan Mark and Kit Wright.

Preliminary panel of judges: Christopher Bantick, Lynn Barclay, Richard Brookfield, Linda Hoare, Anna Hopewell, Barry Maybury, Timothy Rogers, Betty Rosen, Professor Harold Rosen, Sheila Shannon and Anthony Weeks-Pearson.

A SPECIAL BOND

Anthony Lees (10)

Yuk-Fun Liu (14)

William Hedges (6)

The Prince's name is Arthur

The prince's name is Arthur. He is very handsome and smart. He has one sister (smaller than him). On Monday he hunts deer. Tuesday ducks. Wednesday pigs. Thursday cows. Friday doesn't hunt but he has marzipan. Saturday marzipan. Sunday special lunch roast pig. He has a red cloak a gold belt (black boots) a gold medal with red ribbon. A long sword, bow and arrows and a band of men and a lovely father and mother.

Christopher Jennings (14)

*Living in the Shadow of a Genius

WOLFGANG: (*humming* Eine Kleine Nachtmusik) If anyone still alive has the right to hum that, it is me. Who am I? Franz Xavier Wolfgang Amadeus Mozart. Yes, you guessed it! The son of the greatest genius that ever lived.

(*He moves down centre where a table with a glass and a bottle of wine sit. He pours himself a glass and drinks. Relaxed, he starts talking.*)

I was born on the twenty-sixth of July in 1791 when the French Revolution was still in its infancy. I was the second son of the 'Great' Mozart and being born only five months before he died, I have no recollection of him at all. My poor mother, Constanza, was devastated, Herr Mozart was her life; but nevertheless she remarried soon after. She married a soldier, Georg von Nissen, a nice man in a way, but also very stubborn. He began, with Mamma's help, to write a biography of Herr Mozart and it was soon published. By this time I had already decided I was to pursue music as a career and Mamma encouraged me. As a young boy I had shown considerable talent (or so I was told) and was easily persuaded to choose music as my life; the name of Mozart was thought of as an advantage to me by many friends. Little did I know then that a musician is not judged by his own talents but by his background. Presently I began to perform the piano – I hated it! All those people! All eyes on me. I didn't like that at all. I didn't want that at all. I didn't want to be noticed, I wanted to slip into an obscure little corner where no one could see, away from attention. But Mamma disagreed. 'If you're serious about being a musician,' she told me, 'you have to be constantly in the public eye or they will forget you, like they did Wolfgang.' But I argued back, 'Herr Mozart was not forgotten, merely neglected.' I spoke of my father as 'Herr Mozart' because I knew Mamma didn't like that. But how could I call a father I'd never known 'Papa'? Now that 'Herr Mozart' was dead he was thought to be a saint, a martyr. People queued up to see Mamma, the wife of the greatest composer who ever lived. But it was all too late now. Herr Mozart was dead. His fame came after his death. The people who had hated and neglected him when he was alive were all making money from him and his memory. It was unthinkable, and nobody raised a hand to stop them! My father was my only claim to fame. But once people discovered that I didn't remember him, I was forgotten, they had no interest in one who didn't know.

My mother died last year, it was a peaceful death, thank God. She died in her sleep. Just as her troubles ended mine seemed to begin. I travelled to Lvov in Poland where I began my career in earnest, not many people had heard of Herr Mozart there, so I enjoyed a moderate success, but everywhere else I went, as soon as my music was heard, people lost interest. True, my work showed no particular great talent, but nevertheless if my name had been Schmidt I would have been famous. Mozart, my name, was a burden. It was a

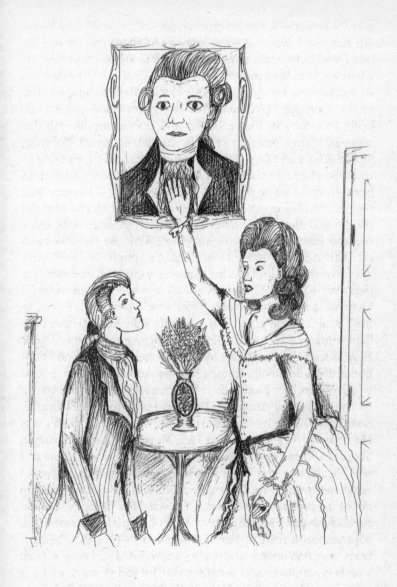

Yuk-Fun Liu (14)

curse, a cross to be carried through life and beyond. God hated me, that much was true, or at any rate he didn't respect me. To him I was but a mere amusement, something to cheer him up when his workload proved heavy. How dare he! How dare he sit and laugh at my struggles. One day I will show him, and the world! 'One day,' I vowed. That day never came and it's not likely to either. In future books and poems my life will be summed up in a sentence: 'He also had a son named Wolfgang Junior'. That's all I'll go down in history for, nothing else. There was talk, of course, there always is. My father, Herr Mozart, had been away for some time and when he returned Mamma was pregnant with me. Of course gossip and lies spread like the plague and soon talk arose about my legitimacy. 'Why did I bear no resemblance to my parents?' 'Why did Mamma insist on naming me after Herr Mozart's pupil Franz Xavier Sussmayer?' Could it be? The whispers were loud and clear for everyone to hear. 'She's had an affair while he was away,' I imagine them to have said. 'Got herself pregnant. Trying to hush it up.' Mamma, to be on the safe side and stop the prattlers, renamed me Franz Xavier Wolfgang Amadeus Mozart! Herr Mozart did not doubt Mamma's word and paid no attention to the idle gossip. In turn Mamma kept a low profile for a while. When Herr Mozart died Herr Sussmayer was thrown out of the house by Mamma. This gave rise to more scandal. Sometimes I wish it were true, the talk, sometimes I wish I was Herr Sussmayer's son and not Herr Mozart's. Although I dream about it I know it's not true. Even if it were, it would mean I was illegitimate and society, which hates illegitimacy, would reject me even more. Of course there was never any question about my brother, Karl Thomas. He was Herr Mozart's son and he could even REMEMBER him! As soon as people learned this, all attention turned to him. He seemed to love this, being a born attention-seeker and I also appreciated it, being a born attention-shunner. And what's more he didn't want to be a musician either. Lucky old him! He hated music! Still does to the best of my knowledge. He's an Austrian Government official now. No comparison there! He never married, though, which struck me as odd as he had a way with women; I never married either, probably because I didn't have a way with women. (*He laughs.*) It's my birthday today. I'm fifty-two years old. In eighteen years' time I'll be double Herr Mozart's age. I haven't told anyone, just a few friends. All I got from Karl was a letter wishing me every happiness. Every happiness? That's a laugh! It's my birthday, I'm fifty-two and I'm stuck in Lvov, Poland. Next year it'll be different, I'll be in Karlsbad. But next year is next year. All I've got now to cheer me up is a glass of wine and a Viennese whirl; hardly Gourmet but it'll have to do. I wonder what my real birth was like, Mamma lying there, the midwife and Herr Mozart looking on. Or, at least I presume he was looking on, unless he was at some concert or other. It's amazing how a dead man, a corpse, can influence your entire life, especially if you have no recollection of him as I with Herr Mozart. His spirit haunts me everywhere, it follows me about like a shadow. And I hate that shadow, I spit on it. (*Relaxing.*) Poor old Herr Mozart! I do blame rather a lot on him. Was it all his fault? Was he that bad? Sometimes in a fury I even curse his name instead of God's. I have scant knowledge of Herr Mozart's life although being his son I am expected to be a mine of information. I have read a few books about him and heard his music but nothing else. Mamma rarely mentioned him, except when it concerned money, which was her favourite subject. She considered it sentimental to reflect on times past and only wanted to make money from him. When I confronted her with this side of her character in an argument one day she spat back,

'One has to be practical!'

Perhaps I am being unfair to her as well. I don't know anything any more. Just as no one knows where Herr Mozart is buried I don't know where my loyalty lies, to my mother? Or to my father's name. Mother, being the nice woman she was, didn't feel any great attachment to past bearers of the name Mozart. Poor old grandpa Leopold Mozart was dug out of the family grave to make room for her relatives' remains. Leopold, Anna Maria and Nannerl, all forgotten relatives of mine. Leopold and Anna Maria were dead before my lifetime began and Nannerl was forbidden ground. Mamma refused me permission to visit her, disapproving strongly of her dead husband's sister. Apparently they had fallen out, or to be more precise, never really fallen in. From what I have heard of Leopold, he was a horrible man. He exploited his children, forcing them into a gruelling tour of Europe. In fact I'm glad he's dead, for if he weren't I would surely be one of his 'precious darlings' dragged around the world unwillingly.

I blame him for Mozart's early death. All the illnesses accumulated on the tour most definitely contributed to Herr Mozart's death. Maybe, if it wasn't for Leopold my life would have been different. Herr Mozart would have been there, I may even have called him 'Papa'. If it weren't for Leopold, Herr Mozart would have taught me, helped me and made me into something. But of course if it weren't for Leopold Mozart Herr Mozart wouldn't have been the great prodigy and genius he was. There's always two ways of looking at something. How can I really blame someone who died before I was even born for my own failure? I'm sure even if my name *was* Schmidt I would still be a failure in music! I suppose it's unfair really to blame your own name for your own failure. I was more of a let down to the name of Mozart than it was to me. (*He chuckles.*) At home we used to have a dusty old copy of Leopold's book *Violinschule* known as the 'Violin Bible' to his contemporaries. It was an acclaimed masterpiece; no one read it, of course, apart from Herr Mozart, but when he was gone it was sold. All that remained in our possession connected with Leopold's memory was exchanged for a few schillings. It was disgraceful really, but since my mother died I've bought a copy and really it has changed my life. I've realised that the Mozart name is an honour to be carried shoulder-high, not a burden carried on the back, even if I do forget it sometimes. With ancestors like Leopold and Herr Mozart I cannot fail to be proud of my family history. Although it *has* brought me more trouble than good, the name of Mozart is mine, however unworthy of it I may be. I am a fool, really, to think that my pathetic, wailing music could ever be enjoyed by the general public, especially when it's compared to the soft seductive tones of Herr Mozart's. But why couldn't I have been something simple, boring and normal like a bank clerk? Probably because that kind of thing *is* boring, and anyway I'm not very good at it. I am of an artistic temperament. (*He laughs.*) Listen to me! I sound like Voltaire! I am not an artist, it is only pretence! How could a buffoon like me ever hope even to attempt to reach the great heights achieved by such composers as Herr Mozart, Herr Beethoven and Herr Schubert? I'm not even in their class. Too low for that! Stop, stop, stop! Now I'm being *too* modest for my own good. I may not be very good but sometimes I do underestimate myself. No matter how hard it is though, I must go on. No one but me will ever know what it is like to live in the shadow of a genius, no one. No one at all.

But enough of such ravings, I must enjoy my birthday, sit back and enjoy it. Alone. All alone.

(*Franz Wolfgang Amadeus Mozart did not live to see his fifty-third birthday.*)

Sophie Nelson (7)

My Papa (Dad)

I love my papa. I adore him, our friendship will never break, even when we hate each other, we forget about it soon. And so we are friends again. He always understands me. And I understand him. He has lovely black soft hair, and lots of bristles so I don't kiss him that much. But I still love him. He

Heather Anderson (8)

sometimes gives me spellings and I try to succeed. My papa is a real man – he's brilliant. He never goes anywhere without a smile, he's normally asleep, and Clare and Hilary would be downstairs watching TV and I would be at Leos (my pony) with Mummy.

Papa is handsome and sometimes vain. I like him when he shaves extra time, and his bristles have gone and they only grow back when he comes home which is in the night, so it's okay. Sometimes Papa reads me a chapter of *Pilgrim's Progress*, and then I read him the next chapter. Papa's a real gentleman. He's ever so pleasing, but when he is grouchy he is mad so I would be quiet. He used to have a beard but he doesn't now, just like he used to smoke but he hates the habit now. He's a good cook. The best man cook in the world. He's brilliant.

Sara Worts (12)

*Granny Scotland

We met again at the wedding.
She seemed so glad.
To me she was so old. Yet . . .
death seemed years away from one
who was so young at heart.
She sat on a long couch,
listening intently to talk.
Dad offered her a drink
'I'll have a large whisky,' she replied.
She held the glass so tightly
it seemed as if inside were all her possessions.
The room soon filled with smoke.
Black clouds floated about,
so we went into the disco.
I turned to find her.
She was dancing,
her green dress sparkling in the lights
as they flashed.
We danced until late.
As we left, I kissed her.
She smelt so strongly of lavender
that I had to sneeze.
Later . . .
Mum said it was probably to cover up
the scent of her . . .
Whisky!

Elizabeth Mann (10)

Hannah Llewellyn (6)

Laughing

When my brother tickles me I laugh and when he tells me jokes I laugh and my face goes all red. When my Mummy does a funny sneeze it makes me laugh and I fall back. When I lie by my dog he licks my hand and I have tears come down my face and I scream and shout and I can't speak when my Dad throws me up in the air I laugh and my eyes shut and my tummy goes tight.

Terry Trappett (7)

Francis Vale (10)

Peter Dawson (5)

*My Sister's Party

Our balloon man had yellow wool hair
and both of his arms came off and one leg.
We bit for apples out of a bucket
And everyone got wet
But not Trishna but most of all Melanie
She duck her head right in
I had an apple with ice over
Hannah made them out of toffee
With stretchy threads like spiders.

14

Katherine Bavage (6)

15

Barnaby Lankester-Owen (12)

Noushin Sorayyapour (11)

*Amoo Afshar

I remember Amoo Afshar
As a kind but quiet man.
He used to come and cut our grapes
When they had finished growing.

I was about five years old
And he used to pretend
That Sebastian, his grandson,
Wanted to marry me.
He had a ring,
Would I like to try it on?

Amoo Afshar wore mainly grey
And a large round hat.

He was very tall and he always used to wear
A very long navy overcoat.
He carried a long umbrella
With a wooden handle.

Amoo Afshar also had grey hair
And brown, dark brown eyes.

I love Amoo Afshar,
I miss him very much.
He isn't here to cut our grapes
Or even tell us stories.

I miss the kind and quiet man,
Amoo Afshar.

William Mair (12)

*Broken Friends

They sit on the wall,
its maroon bricks crumbling where they sit,
always exactly on the same spot.
The mortar falls,
exploding where it lands,
silent,
unheard under the continuous
mumbling of the two old men.
Talking in their own language: Pigeon double-dutch.
They have been two life-long friends.
And always will be.
But, they are so different . . .

Victoria Picard (11)

One walks, slowly, feeling age.
He walks along lanes, roads and footpaths,
never stopping, except at the wall.
He is tall and bony.
Matted grey hair like wire wool
hides under his old flat cap.
His shoes are
black clown's shoes,
the toes blown up in a bubble
worn on one side from how he walks,
a clown's stupid walk,
hobbling from left to right,
left to right . . .
a fearful baby, rocking itself.

His breath whirls from his mouth,
smelling of his last meal,
soup,
vegetable soup from Meals on Wheels.

The other is more cheerful,
rosy cheeks and always a smile.
He likes mending and making.
I bring him my bike,
its wheel flat from a thorn.
His hands quickly get to work
twisting and turning,
rheumatism or no rheumatism.
He smiles, happy to be of use.
When finished, he wheels it up our drive,
gives it to me,
and then thrusts a small bundle into my hands.
Wine Gums, wrapped in kitchen roll.
His present to me
although it should be vice versa.

One day he died,
his rosy cheeks white
and his smile faded.

His friend still walks,
slower now,
never stopping at the wall.

Julie Magill (13)

My Aunt Jean

'Now, Julie,' said Mum, as she left me across the road. 'Be a good girl and I'll come and collect you at five past seven.'

Mum then went back across the road and I paddled up the street.

This is my earliest memory of Auntie Jean. I was going to her house for dinner. We were living in Belfast at the time and Auntie Jean only lived up the street.

I, a little (or not so little) four-year-old, closed the gate and skipped up the drive. Auntie Jean was waiting for me.

We played our usual games that day. Auntie Jean got out the 'toys' (which were just a bag of old ornaments and things that would interest a child). Auntie Jean sat there knitting; she loved knitting and sewing and had made me quite a few dresses for my dolls.

After I got tired of playing with the ornaments I sat up on the sofa beside her. We then played the 'talking game'. I mouthed silly nonsense sentences like: 'There is a horse in a purple tree.' Auntie Jean, though she couldn't make out what I was saying, always replied quite seriously with remarks such as: 'Well, Granny didn't tell me that!'

Then it was time for tea. I always loved having tea with Auntie Jean. We usually had stew. You may say to yourself, 'How boring,' but Auntie Jean was a wonderful cook and made the loveliest stew that you could ever taste.

When dinner was over, we went and sat by the fire in the living room and sang little songs. Our three favourites were:

> 'There ain't no sense,
> Sittin' on a fence,
> All by yourself in the moonlight.'

and:

'My Aunt Jean,
She called me in
And gave me tea
Out of her wee tin.

Half a bap,
With sugar on the top
And three black lumps,
Out of her wee shop.'

and:

'Mersey Dotes and Dozey Dotes,
And little Lambsey Ivy,
Skiddely Divie too.
Wouldn't you?'

After reading me an 'Oor Wullie' story from the newspaper, Aunt Jean told me the stories of the things that my Granny did when she was little; for she was Granny's aunt, not mine. Then Mum came to pick me up.

My most vivid memory of Aunt Jean is rather a sad one. A year after we moved back to Coleraine, Auntie Jean followed and then so did Granny May and Granda Bob.

One day in 1984, I was told that Auntie Jean was going to the Royal Victoria Hospital in Belfast. I didn't know she was being rushed there.

Not long after this I overheard Mum say something about an old peoples' home, or something like that. I still didn't understand.

The following Sunday, I was brought down to see her. I was excited because I was seeing her after a whole week.

When I arrived in Auntie Jean's ward I was shocked at what I saw. There was Auntie Jean – my AUNTIE JEAN – with all sorts of horrible tubes sticking into her.

I looked up at Granny. She smiled softly.

'Can I talk to her now?' I asked hopefully.

'Yes, dear. But Auntie Jean can't talk back,' she replied.

I walked over to the hospital bed and put my face close to Auntie Jean's.

'I'm here, Auntie Jean,' I whispered. 'It's Julie.'

Then the nurse came and said that we would have to go. At six years old I didn't realise how sick she really was.

I kissed her cheek and said, 'Bye-bye.' Then we left the hospital.

I awoke to hear the birds singing that warm August morning. As I lay and thought I remembered Aunt Jean in the hospital. Dad had brought me to see her, and Granny said she couldn't talk but I knew she heard me – I just knew it. She would get better soon.

'It's too early to get up,' I thought and I turned over in bed and went back to sleep.

Everyone was crying when I walked into the kitchen later on that day. It was Auntie Jean; she was dead! She had died quietly early that same morning.

I stared blankly as the memories came flooding back to me. Stew and 'toys' and 'talking games' and songs, the 'Oor Wullie' stories and the hospital. A lump came into my throat. I burst into tears and ran from the room.

Even now, six years later, I am not completely separated from Auntie Jean. For though I can't see her, nor hear her, I can remember the little things that no one else can remember; think of all the kind things she said and did. They will stick in my mind for ever and I will never forget her. For when there are memories two souls can never be parted.

Alison Toward (12)

My Granpa

Despite the wall I had managed to build around myself pieces kept breaking off and I was faced with the fact that my granpa wasn't coming back. Why though? He was my granpa. He'd never done anything wrong in his life.

When he was in hospital I was scared of him. I felt guilty. He was my granpa. I'd known him all my life and yet now when he needed me most I was terrified of him.

It just all felt different. He reached out to me and I ran to him but more out of fear than love. At that moment it suddenly hit me that he wasn't just my granpa he was a husband and a father.

Everybody was crying and all I could do was offer them sweets as if it would help. They were all ignoring me. My granpa would never do this. I was always the centre of attention – after all, I was the youngest. This is what drew that special bond between granpa and me.

Even my brother didn't mind if I had more sweets than him. I was in a room filled with people I'd known all my life yet now they all seemed like strangers.

My mum tried to explain that God had taken him away. But when is he coming back? I kept asking my mum. When my mum replied never, I felt this snake seething with hatred creep inside my body. Who's God anyway? Why should he have my granpa?

Ena Mgbomo (13)

Lucienne Kidd (10)

*My Father

The sun goes down
So I turn around,
And there I see my father;
The loving tender man who walks,
who speaks to me.
I sought him
And found him
And I'll stand by him for ever;
For he is the ghost who walks
Through time and space;
For he is within me
Wherever I go;
He is the blood and soul
In my heart;
He is the one I treasure
For ever;
The one who keeps me going;
The one I love and cherish.

AS IF THE WORLD HAS STOPPED BREATHING FOR A MOMENT

Allan Mackenzie (11)

Barry O'Neill (10)

*Something happened very suddenly

It all started after my dinner at seven o'clock in the evening. I went to watch TV in the sitting room. After I had gone in my sister Connie and my Daddy came in to see what was on TV, they had nothing else to do. My Mummy was in the kitchen cleaning up the breakfast bar, when my Uncle Desmond came into the house to get his coat. My Mummy went up the stairs to get his coat, because he would wake the baby up from her sleep. I did not say goodbye to him. The next morning I got out of bed and my Mummy said, 'There has been two people shot dead and we think one of them is your Uncle Desmond.' I did not want to go to school that day. My Mummy said, 'We will pick you up if it is.' My Daddy came in that day and took me out of school at break-time and took me and my sister and told me that it was my Uncle Desmond. I loved my Uncle Desmond. It happened very suddenly.

Emma Forrest (14)

*The Dictator

War is a model in high heels,
Beautiful and important,
Mesmerising,
Dictating the fashion.

Fashion is a dictator in high heels,
Ousted eventually,
Only to leave space,
For the next ambitious oddity.

Occasionally war trips on its heels,
But picks itself up off the floor,
Dusts itself down,
And resolves to have those shoes mended.

War always looks better,
With mascara on.

Noushin Sorayyapour (11)

*The Peace Lily

The lily is like a swan trying to speak
But the bigger ones are practically attacking him,
Stopping him because he is the youngest.
The reeds are bullying everyone.
Today they are so unkind,
They talk amongst themselves
And he is crying.
The reeds pull him down.
He is dying.

Barnaby Lankester-Owen (12)

William Mair (12)

*Hare

His nose twitches,
three tiny olives in the shape of a pie chart.
He smells the strong scent
of Wild Mushrooms.
Before he was born his world was black,
black as the wayward sheep.
Nothing to smell or see.

Dawn Lee (12)

Now he is overwhelmed.
Now, for the first time, his heart
clashes with his mother's.
His coat, matted with membrane,
dries, crisp in the sun,
like a dog's, fresh from a swim.

Through spring he grows,
his coat glows gold.
His ears stand firm,
like two heads from wooden spoons.
His eyes focus in the light
and from them shines his youth.
The muscles in his legs strengthen
and his speed, like his mother's,
is miraculous.

As he runs, there is a click in the undergrowth,
a second to aim, then . . .
Crack!
A shot like a dropping pan
fills the clearing.

An ear-splitting cry,
like the highest note
on the most out of tune violin . . .

The hare falls.
Dying, he returns to the darkness.

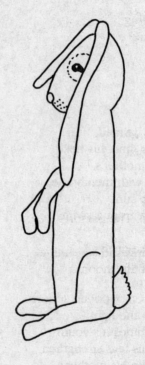

Georgina Hucker (13)

Sarah Fletcher (8)

*Did You See That Light?

Did you see that light
In the dusty window
Of the porch? Did you see it
In the cold damp wood?
Who was there? Was it a
Robber or bandit?

Was there noise
Shouting, screaming
Banging, twanging?
Tell me the story
Of that afternoon.

A long story
To tell, my child.
But I'll tell you now
The answer to what
You say.

I did see it in the
Cold damp wood. The person,
It was a robber.
There was shouting and screaming
And banging that afternoon.

Dina Garcia (12)

Bad Back

I wish I could
Unscrew my vertebrae
And flop around
With my head
Between my
Legs,
Then lie on
A hard,
Hard board,
Flat on the floor.

Samantha Scriven (11)

My Grandma

My Great Grandma,
Eighty-seven years or more,
Sits by the window,
Holding needles in wrinkled hands,
Her loose skin in folds of silk,
Cold tea at her side.

With the cup, I go to the kitchen.
A stuffy smell hits me.
I open a window.
Fresh air.
Then thump, thump and
In comes Grandma.

Gemma Townsend (12)

Then later in the Committee room,
I sit watching some fish,
Silver like lightning,
Gold and rusty brown.
Around a table old men play,
Cards all laid out,
Faces dull with a bad hand
But on some, a sneaky grin.

My Gran, a little way off, sits with a friend.
She talks, her friend's face like cling-film.
Then back,
Back to the stuffy heat and boiled cabbage.

Calum Brown (8)

*The Old Woman

Sitting
In that very same chair
In the very same room
At the same time, any time
As if she would wait for decay
Just waiting
Waiting
Drifting
Dying
In that very same chair
She would watch the Christmasses
Drift past
Just giving thanks
And doing nothing else
Till she passed away
In that very same chair
In the very same room

Jessica Macfarlane (12)

Joanne Ireland (14)

Time

My Grandma lived in a basement flat.
I imagined it as an underground hole,
And my Grandma, a creature, hiding scared
From the outside world.
Caught in time.
The staircase bent around
Like a huge Chinese Dragon
With a million bright colours
In the carpet.
The carpet itself was shaggy and heavy . . .
A big, hairy dog could easily get lost in it,
Or so I thought.
From the window two rectangles of light
Melted onto the carpet.
The dust flew,
Caught in those two rays of light,
Caught like Grandma,
Caught in time.
And if I, too, stepped into those rectangles,
Would I be caught forever, like dust?
Would I be caught like Grandma?
For the very last time.

Attia Hussain (15)

*Understanding the Prayer?

Another car drives up to the mosque on a warm Friday
    afternoon,
Another woman steps out,
Another door is opened
As she adjusts her soft black veil.

Then they wait outside the building . . .

The children who have not been told
Continue to chatter,
And some uninformed babies
Continue to cry
Through the melodious call to prayer.

A sudden silence,
As if the world has stopped breathing for a moment,
And then the prayer begins,
Now soft and controlled,
Now loud and passionate,
Now they're moved to tears –
The brightly clothed figures
Still veiled in black
Seem to move in harmony with the words.

But there in the corner
Sits one lonely teenager,
Too embarrassed to admit
That she cannot feel or understand
This foreign language
That should be natural to her.

At the end the congregation arise.

Some hunt for their children
Hiding behind piled-up chairs,
Others greet welcoming friends
With honest laughter.

But she says nothing,
And with a timid smile
Walks past the chattering groups,
Slips away from sight.

BREAKING THE SURFACE

David Lewis (11)

Suzanne Alderton (12)

Dream of the Fisherman

The line sways in the breeze.
On the end,
A bright orange float.
There is a tug.
A tug of strength,
As if gravitation pulls on the sea.
Then,
In a flash of light,
Silver leaps from the lake,
And lands on the bank,
Where flames form a circle.
This fish is a demon.
The sea demon.

Matthew King (11)

Wayne Brooks (12)

It darts,
And with a flap of its fins
It is a bird,
Beak shimmering like petrol in a puddle.
Each scale is a feather,
A raindrop on a window.
It swoops
Back into the sea,
Its world forever.
I wake
To find mist merging over the lake,
And I leave,
With an empty net
But a full mind.

Christopher Austin (11)

43

Jessica Brown (12)

Rockpool Reflection

Morning came.
Red rays threw the water picture.
The pinky sun hung from the weed on the bottom,
Its heat too great and harsh.
Cold water fought back,
And the heat sizzled out on the surface.
Where a faint rainbow
Filtered on the back of the crab
Whose claws clutched the light grey clouds.
The gulls floated,
breaking the surface,
but without a quiver.
On the stones lay little barnacles
From the sky's many-a-face.
The salty breeze backcombed my hair.
And the surface rippled.
I looked up and the clouds smiled
and melted away.
Just like the images in the rockpool.

Matilda Taylor (11)

Gemma White (12)

Reflections

John Thrower (12)

The rushes on the banks of the lake
Stretch out to touch.
The reflection of the old mansion
Is so still . . .
A painting,
A perfect mirror image.

A pond skater on a lily
Pulls on his boots,
Laces tight.
Off he goes.
He spins around and around,
Dancing on his reflection,
Stretching it.

A frog jumps.
The water pot spills,
The painting runs.

Calum Brown (8)

*Under-water

Diving into the welcoming water,
Rays of light from the autumn sun shadowing the ruffled pool,
On one side the small cascade,
Silvery rocks covered in slippery green moss,
On the other the continuous lapping of water going on its way.
I kick dive to the bottom,
Around me swirling algae, all shapes and sizes,
Tree leaves floating above,
Curling stones, nearly sediment now,
Sweeping moss
Big black-green rocks like mounds of soil,
I brush my hand against them,
A soft, joyful feeling,
The cascade that used to be a current of angry water
Now just millions of bubbles tickling my face,
I go through my father's legs and break surface,
Remembering the awesome under-water sights.

Sarah Naylor (8)

Suzanne Alderton (12)

Stream Reflections

The water slowly moves downstream,
Stretching my reflection,
Like dough,
Rolled by a baker.
Clouds above my head
Form a maze for the fish
Who dart between them,
And, as a swan
Swims past the sun,
Both of his beaks touch
In the centre of the hazy circle,
Causing it to crinkle
Like the bark of a beech tree,
Struck by moonbeams.
A fisherman casts his line.
The fluorescent orange float
Lands in the hawthorn hedge.
Maybe fixed there forever,
Like the reflections
In that slow-moving stream.

Marie Coby (12)

Kelly Waters (12)

Jessica Brown (12)

Seal

On the sand by the rippling water
his coat gleamed in the moonlight
as if coated in thin silver.
Or had dust fallen from the star overhead?
He slid into the water,
easily,
as if covered in grease.
Oily colours drifted in the waves
and the moon's rays threw lasers
through the night sky.
Webbed paws were his paddles,
racing his clay body away from the hunter.
The star beckoned him on.
And he followed the light once more.

Michelle Hurr (13)

Adam Dale (12)

*The Fish Wars

The pond shone majestically as Andrew sat down beside it, it sparkled with small animals going this way and that and seemed to look up at him like a hamster looks at its paycheck. Andrew was fishing, he spent his whole life fishing, he would eat then fish, eat then fish, eat then fish then sleep. That was the pattern of his life. He lived to fish and he didn't fish to live and he was perfectly contented that way.

He hadn't caught anything but he wasn't expecting to, he hadn't caught anything for twenty years. Andrew was twenty years old. He was happy just sitting on a stool, wearing a silly jumper and not doing much, that was the way of the fisher, that was the way of Andrew.

Sometimes people would come fishing with him and ruin his day and he always felt out of place with them, he used to buy computer magazines and constantly talk about X-TALK SHOW HOST 19 and other boring games but that only frightened away the sensible people, not the fishers, not people like him. He normally went to the pond, where no one would find him, where he would lie back and look into the stars and dream about fish, about Haddock and Trout and Minnow and Sole and Antelope, he would dream about meeting them, about playing cards with them, about touching noses with them, but he would never dream about eating them or catching them, he didn't eat fish and fish didn't eat him and that was fine.

Once in his lifetime he had got a bite but he had released it before he wound it in. If it wasn't on the surface or held by him then it didn't count as a catch, he had felt terribly distressed about harming the fish and so had taken the hook off. He had never put it on again, just in case. It was time for supper, he took out his sandwich and ate it, he fished. Two feet below him a fish was dying, it was dying because it was supposed to die, it was supposed to have been caught in a hook and perished but there was no hook to perish by. So here he was, dying, for no reason, prematurely, all because the stupid fisherman up there had taken the hook off, all because of one stupid fish which had been caught once, and here all of the fish would die, unless one of them got caught by the stupid fisherman, the fish looked up, he looked down, he looked up again and he died.

Not long after his death, a fish entered the rock where the dead fish had lived, he saw the body floating on top of the ceiling, he panicked and swam along the riverbottom to tell his friends about the death, unluckily he was feeling quite hungry and he swam past the piece of string on which a hook was supposed to be, on which a worm was supposed to be skewered, he started bleeding, he died, along came his friend, she died, along came her friend.

It was 9.00 p.m. and all was supposed to be well, unluckily it wasn't.

Andrew was asleep, he was asleep on the stool, it was the way of the fisher, the fish were dying, caught by invisible hooks, it was the way of the fish, the cow was tap-dancing in Norway but stopped because it felt a bit silly, it chewed grass, that was the way of the cow.

Andrew woke up to a fine summer morning, slightly cold but not much, the smell of absolutely nothing drifted up his nose and the sweet song of the bird didn't come to his ears, there were no fishermen on the banks and no cars. Andrew felt wonderful, so he spoke.

He hadn't spoken for ten years because he found speaking rather tedious and he didn't have anyone to speak to, but he had the urge to speak now so he said the only word he knew, the only word he actually ever said in his life.

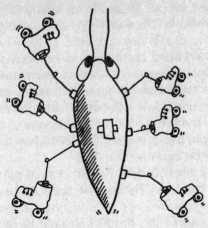

Jo Linney (11)

'Fish,' he said.

He could feel the word floating up into the sky, he could feel it warming up his whole body, he could see it run around the fields, where he noticed that no cows were grazing. He decided to get some breakfast before he fished.

He entered the shop.

'Good morning, sir, can I help you?' said an elderly gentleman who looked like the owner of the shop because he had just asked if he could help and that would have been pretty strange if he wasn't the owner and he was just a law-abiding modern citizen which Andrew thought he wasn't because he was wearing a toga.

'Fish,' said Andrew.

'Then you want some kind of sandwich,' said the elderly gentleman and reached for an onion bhajee sandwich, almost knocking his laurel wreath off.

Andrew looked round for other people and didn't see any.

When he turned back, the gentleman was gone. He looked around, no one anywhere, he went out of the shop.

'Supermarket next,' he thought and tottered off.

On his way to the supermarket a few houses exploded and a car started making faces at him but he ignored everything, it was the law of the fisher.

Before he knew it he was in the country. Leaning against a fence quietly humming to itself was a cow, it began to sing.

'I will fly a yellow paper sun in your sky,' it sang.

Andrew said, 'Thank you' and 'Much obliged' and blushed.

'When the wind is high,' it carried on.

'When the wind is high.

I will float a silver silver moon near your window.

If your night is dark.

If your night is dark.

In letters of hope on a snow-white kite,

I will write "I love you".

And send it soaring high above you.

For all to read.'

Large clapping from a distance bounced into Andrew's ears and Andrew clapped as well, the cow took a bow and walked off into a large car which had suddenly appeared next to Andrew, the car drove off.

Andrew forgot breakfast and clambered back to his pond, where, on a small rock jutting out from the pond, sat a fish, it glared at him menacingly and solemnly passed a hook to Andrew, he refused it and smiled.

'Thank you anyway,' he said and realised that he had been speaking to the cow and hadn't mentioned fish at all.

The fish shoved the hook into Andrew's hand and opened his mouth, he took another hook and pretended to hook it into his mouth, he nodded patronisingly.

'It's terribly easy,' he said.

'This fish has the subtlety of a French cooker,' thought Andrew, but he politely replied, 'Go away.' It was then that the fish started leaping at him.

I DON'T KNOW IF YOU GET THIS FEELING BUT I ALWAYS DO, IT'S THAT ONE THAT YOU GET WHEN YOU'RE SHOPPING AND ALL THESE PIGS START TO PROD YOU AND LOOK IN COOKERY BOOKS AND LICK THEIR LIPS. IT'S THAT FEELING OF DOORKNOBS SLOWLY TURNING YOU ROUND, THAT FEELING OF CATS PICKING YOU UP AND TICKLING YOUR CHIN, IT'S THAT FEELING OF TYPEWRITERS DOING NOTHING, OF DISTANT BELLS IN SUMMER. ANYWAY, BACK TO THE STORY.

The fish had determination in its eyes and was desperately lunging itself at the hook which Andrew held. Andrew dropped it. The fish looked up at him.

'Spoilsport,' it said and died.

Andrew took control of himself, he didn't understand what was happening so he sneezed and put it down to religion, he decided that the best thing to do would be to run.

He ran.

He ran.

He ran.

He suddenly realised that he was getting nowhere. He looked around him, there was nothing, there wasn't blackness, there wasn't whiteness, there was so much nothing that there wasn't any colour at all. There was just him and about a thousand fish. They were all screaming out things like 'CATCH ME' and 'WOULD YOU JUST MIND FIXING THIS HOOK INTO MY MOUTH AND REELING ME IN?' and 'YOU MIGHT AS WELL CATCH ONE OF US, YOU'VE ALREADY TOTALLY DESTROYED THE ENTIRE HUMAN RACE AND WIPED OUT EARTH, ALL ITS LIVING INHABITANTS AND DOOMED ABOUT FIVE HUNDRED AND SIXTY OTHER WORLDS SO BE A GOOD SPORT.'

Andrew suddenly realised what was wrong. He had broken the law of the fisher, he had taken the hook from the rod. And now he had wiped out everything and probably done something terribly naughty like open up a wormhole in the space-time continuum flow and ripped the fabrics of existence as he knew it, which wasn't much at all.

So he did something that he had never done before, he took a nearby hook and grabbed a nearby fish and . . .

Andrew woke up with a start, he was at the side of the pond humaning, that was what he always did, eat then human, eat then human, eat then human then sleep, that was his pattern, he lived to human and didn't human to live. Some said that he was a very boring fish.

FIN

Hannah Sullivan (12)

The Bath Houses

This is an account of an incident that stands out in my mother's memory. The story was compiled by questioning my mother and grandmother, and then putting this information together. To make it less clumsy for the reader I have written it in the first person.

When I was young, we lived in one of the rows upon rows of terraced houses which snaked up and down the hills of Sheffield. These houses were all the same. From the outside, sparkling clean windows revealed crisp white net curtains. Each doorstep was scrubbed scrupulously clean, and the edges whitened to stand out at night. After you opened the door from the pavement there was a small front room, and then directly behind this, a kitchen. This room was also small and had two doors; one down to the cellar, and the other on to the back yard. Across this was a row of toilets – one for each house. Upstairs was bedrooms and an attic.

You will see from this description there was something

missing – a bathroom. To go to the toilet entailed a dash or saunter (depending on the weather) across the yard, but how did we bathe? Well the answers were varied. The public bath houses were one popular solution.

One Friday evening, near Christmas, and just after I had started Grammar School, my family all decided to go to the bath houses. This was because next day was going to be a large family wedding, and I was going to be a bridesmaid.

It was getting dark as we set off. I felt a little nervous, but very grown up too, as my mother, father and myself all walked down the street. I knew the way well, as our destination was in the same building as the swimming pool. The building was large with blackened stone, and above the door was the Sheffield City crest.

Once inside, my father paid at the kiosk and we were each given tickets. I clutched in my hand a small rectangular sachet of lurid orange shampoo. These were the days when natural things were scorned, and this looked suitably full of chemicals.

My father then went down one corridor, and my mother and I down another. It had been dusky outside, and my first impression was of seemingly endless bright white tiles. We came to a corner, turned, and were hit by warmth, steam and laughter. There were several large ladies in starched white gowns. They looked very much alike to me as no hair was showing, only beaming red faces under white hats. My mother was worried that I would do something wrong, and incur the wrath of the white giants. On our way, there had been some discussion between my mother and father as to whether I was old enough to go in on my own. In his own quiet way my father had won. I travelled a long journey each day on my own, and he pointed out I was therefore old enough to go into a bath cubicle on my own!

My mother turned away from hissing her last instruction, 'Make sure you rinse your hair properly,' and with an ingratiating smile proffered her ticket to the chief white giant. She was given a large towel and a small bar of soap and sent to a

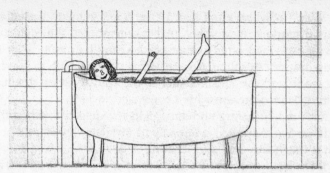

Hannah Sullivan (12)

distant cubicle. In my turn I was given the same, and the lady gently led me to cubicle nineteen. She had a nice smile on her face but I was intrigued by the coarseness and heaviness of the towel and longed to read the embroidered letters on it.

I remember entering my cubicle, and the white giant closing the door behind me. Suddenly hot water splashed from the metal pipe into the huge white bath. This galvanised me into action, so I hurriedly undressed and hung my clothes up on the hook and put my shoes under the wooden slatted seat. I spared time though to read the words on the towel: 'Sheffield City Corporation'.

I gingerly got into the bath. It was very hot and as I was small for my age the bath seemed very big. I wondered if I would be able to swim, and tried going under the water. Although it wasn't big enough to swim it was possible to float. I spent a little while doing this. I noticed how everything seemed different from this position. The steam seemed clearer and the lights brighter and the smells stronger. The noises were muffled, but I heard occasional shouts. Sitting up again I was intrigued to hear:

'More hot in number fifteen.'

I decided that I wasn't acting as responsibly and grown up as my father expected, and decided to soap myself thoroughly.

'More hot in seven,' I heard and in amazement carried on soaping myself. It was then that I remembered the sachet of shampoo. I had often before washed my hair with a lot of soap, but not this time. I had to get out of the bath to get the shampoo and was shocked first by the cold and then the heat of the water on re-entering it.

After much tearing and struggling I managed to open the shampoo and applied it liberally to my hair. The exotic perfume was heady and after hearing,

'More hot in twelve,' I heard my own wavering voice say,

'More hot in nineteen, please.'

As soon as I said it I was shocked. I sat still, waiting for either a white giant to rush in and berate me, or my mother, but no, all that happened was another gush of hot water.

It had become very hot now and I had lost all sense of time. So I just had one more short float and then reluctantly hauled myself out of the hot bath. My body certainly looked very clean and pink and as I put my clothes on they seemed to stick uncomfortably. I gathered my belongings and went out of the cubicle. Cooler air hit me, and at least two of the white giants smiled. The greatest shock came, though, after meeting first my mother and then my father when we left the building. It was so cold and dark, and I felt warm and sleepy from the bath. I'll never know how I managed to walk home.

Ashley Coulson (10)

*The Figurehead

Sometimes I mourn the drowned sailors.
Then each spring warms and revives me;
Bright memories burst into life:

Those days in the harbour at first light,
When laughing sailors, cold and wet,
Packed the creaking ship
With cargoes of wheat, wine, oil.
Made ready to travel wide, deep oceans.

'Here, Cleo, take a look!' a young tar called,
'What a fine piece of painted wood you are.
Splendid as a real woman!'
And I saw my face in the scratched glass he held:
Yellow, wavy hair swept boldly back.
Big, bright blue eyes and crimson smiling lips
That challenged the fates at sea.

Many journeys were wild and dangerous!
Winds whipped my face,
Salty tears raked my eyes
The sea roared like an untamed beast.

Sometimes the sky teemed with migrating birds
Making quick manoeuvres,
Flashing like grey-black specks.
Insubstantial clouds like cobwebs
Caught fire from the setting sun.

Later, the night sky calmed me,
And I heard the water's slip-slap against the hull.
Tips of waves sparkled under the stars,
Dark fins broke the sea's surface,
Then disappeared, silent and secret.
Finally sea and sky merged in darkness.

Sometimes I mourn the drowned sailors.
Then each spring warms and revives me;
Bright memories burst into life.

Anna Mitchell (6)

Clouds and the Moon

The moon was racing towards me
Through an archway of clouds
Like a proud horse
Riding the silent clouds.
Dark trees like servants
Bowing before it.

A light shining in the sky
With clouds dancing round it.
The savage moon
Bites the clouds
Bits are ripped up and left.

Long thin strands of cloud
Holding the moon up
To be examined
Like forceps holding a pearl.

Sometimes the sky
Is dull and dark
A curtain of clouds
Is drawn across the moon
And it is time to sleep.

Daniel Lester (13)

Full Circle

The world revolves in endless space
The human race, part of its cargo – most of its strife;
And life itself? The nihilist might say
Is, in a way, like a circle: closed and bound,
A continuous round,
Symbolising
Nothing.

Graham MacPherson (16)

The sphere, since man's earliest endeavour,
However, has been at the centre of our history:
The mystery of Stonehenge's concentric rings
Brings calendar, clock and altar
All made to order
In that shape.

No Darwin's ape, the Neolithic man
Began to reason, raised himself to thought, saw sun rising
And surmising the sun and moon were gods, found
That the round, because of this, was revered most in his mind.
Mankind, it seemed, could take no risks
With discs – a shape omnipotent.

Nicholas Hudson (15)

For Christian too, the circle is a holy sight:
All light, suspended in mid air,
So fair, above the heads of men most righteous – saints,
The artist paints a golden aura which signifies
To the eyes of those who view the work that even if the man
  is lowly,
He is holy in the sight of God
Omnipotent and wise.

Richard Vine (16)

Richard Lobb (14)

Man is always striving for an ultimate goal,
His restless soul can follow many ways pre-set;
Yet money too means power, wealth, corruption
And when it talks, (sans interruption), it just confesses
It possesses the power of life and death,
And like breath and blood and all vital things,
It circulates . . . Pursued no less:

Progress was seen by many as an effort to reach the goal
Of a whole and perfect world within man's sights
When human rights for all would mean no illness, want or
    pain,
Each generation's gain: closer to the ideal 'morrow;
But in sorrow before we reach the brink
Ecologists say, 'Think, turn back before the fall!'
Progress was just a circle after all.

The world revolves in endless space.
The human race, who can't get off, blunder
From revolution to revolution and wonder, 'Are we getting
    anywhere?
Is He there, or is the circle closed and bound,
A continuous round
Symbolising
Nothing?'

NO CODE FOR REACHING
YOU GIVEN

Hayley Goddard (10)

Emma Forrest (14)

*What our Mother was Taught as a Girl

I hate your music.

No you don't,
The only thing you hate,
Is Adolf Hitler.

Yes you hate him too,
But I promise you,
I hate your music.

Well thanks a lot,
I love you too.

True,
But you also love dark chocolate.

Tahira Yaqoob (16)

Adibah

I first met Adibah at a lecture at the local mosque. I gave in to my mother and reluctantly agreed to go, foreseeing a couple of hours spent in boredom. I purposefully strode in late, my head bared in defiance, and slumped into a seat as far from the front of the small room as I could find. I looked around with a bored expression as if to disconnect myself from my surroundings: it was a basement room, badly lit, with white walls and only an old sheet to mute the echo of footsteps on the stone floor. The faces dotted around the room were mainly familiar ones. Finally, I turned my gaze to the front of the room. The first thing that struck me was that the lecturer was white. Dressed in a long, concealing robe, her scarf knotted tightly under her chin, she provided a marked contrast to the brown-skinned girls, dutifully shrouded in their dupattas. Despite myself, I felt curiosity awakening within me. What was she going to talk about? Why was she dressed like that? I didn't have to wait long for an answer. After a few minutes, she stood up, cleared her throat and surveyed her audience with steady grey eyes.

'Let me introduce myself,' she said, in a voice that was neither loud and harsh, nor subdued, but rather, clear and confident. 'My name is Adibah – at least, that is my adopted name. My English friends know me as Alison. That's because until two years ago, I was a passive Christian, and it was at that time that I decided to convert to Islam.'

I sat up suddenly and pricked up my ears in interest.

'What made me convert? Well I was touring countries in the Middle East at the time. I think it was the difference of lifestyle I was first struck with. There I had been, selfishly living my life to suit me, looking no further than what I wanted, and here were whole communities of people, devoting their entire lives to God. Everything they did was with a purpose in mind, whether for religious reasons or charitable ones. It made me feel ashamed because of the useless life I had been living, and because I had always thought of them as a primitive people.'

She went on to say how she had then been attracted by the rich, harmonious sound of the call to prayer, and the beauty of the Arabic manuscripts. She spoke of how religion had filled a void in her life and gave her a sense of fulfilment. Listening to her, I felt an intense dislike, a fear of her, because she was so eloquent, so convincing; because I – the cynicist, the non-believer! – felt ashamed of having doubts, when she was so firm in her faith.

As she spoke, she waved her pale slender hands to convey the depth of her feeling; occasionally, she would steeple her fingers under her chin and look ceilingwards as if summoning some divine power.

'People tend to think of Islam as an institution which stifles women's rights, but I think it merely protects women, while allowing them all the freedom they could want. In fact,' she said, with a little laugh, 'I like to think of myself as a Muslim feminist.'

Immediately, I felt contempt and scorn flood me. Muslim feminist, indeed – what a contradiction in terms! I, who had been brought up in a community which believed that a woman's place lay by rights in the kitchen and in obedience to her husband – I, who knew that this wasn't possible either in theory or practice, could only pity her for being so ignorant and for trusting so blindly and faithfully in what little theoretical implications there were, without seeing that society's attitudes spun on their own axes.

Finally, the talk came to an end. On an impulse, I pushed forward through the people milling around and halted before her.

'Excuse me,' I blurted out, 'but I can't agree with what you were saying about feminism in Islam.'

'Don't you? Why not? But wait – why don't you come to my house one afternoon and we can discuss it properly?'

'Perhaps,' I said, smiling wryly, knowing full well that I had no intention of going.

'How about this Sunday?'

The proposal of a fixed date took me by surprise. I nodded mutely, unable to make an excuse.

'I look forward to it,' she said.

'You'll have to go,' my mother urged.

'I know.'

'I mean, she'll be expecting you.'

'I know.'

I stepped off the bus with a feeling of dread not far removed from that which I had felt before the lecture. It was the height of summer: the sun blazed down with a fierce intensity and reflected harshly off white walls, hurting my eyes.

Nevertheless, Adibah still bore her traditional robe and scarf. She welcomed me as if she had known me all her life. We sat in the shade of her patio, sipping Cokes and enjoying the weather.

'My husband is playing cricket with his friends,' she said.

'You're married?' I exclaimed in surprise.

She smiled. 'I met him when I was trying to find out more about Islam. Don't get me wrong – I'd more or less made up my mind by the time I'd met him.'

The visit was surprisingly pleasant. We talked in earnest about differing beliefs and expectations. I felt a grudging admiration, which soon turned to liking, of her tolerance of my opposing views. In fact, that day was followed by many such more. A close friendship developed that summer, despite the difference in our ages and our conflicting opinions. She was optimistic when I cynically despaired of the human race; I became passionate about issues which were important to me and my quick temper was easily aroused; she was calm and level-headed, yet constant in her beliefs. I confided all that made me hold back from a total religious commitment and she in turn listened patiently and sympathetically, traits which I desperately tried to emulate. Nevertheless, a barrier existed: between her listening to me and understanding what I was saying. I made myself believe it didn't matter: as long as nothing happened to contradict the happy, rosy picture she had created of her new life, she could feel secure. I remember once when she told me in shocked tones that her husband's friends, whom she had thought to be devout Muslims, were regular drinkers.

'Men,' I said grimly, 'are such hypocrites. They preach at their wives and then do the exact opposite.' However, such a revelation only emphasised my fears.

I remember particularly the day Adibah rang me urgently asking me to meet her at a coffee shop we had been to a couple of times. She sounded unusually shaken; I was alarmed by the desperation in her voice and hurried to our meeting place. I found her toying with her coffee. Just the sight of her aimlessly turning her spoon frightened me; it wasn't like her not to have some purpose in mind. I slid into the seat opposite her. For some time, she stared out of the window at the grey-faced people milling about on the grey pavements; then, ashen-faced, she told me in a flat voice how she had discovered that her husband was having an affair; how she had suspected him for some time, but couldn't bring herself to believe it; how she had confronted him and how he had told her he intended to continue seeing his mistress. I do not know how long we sat there; I only remember the feeling of being out of my depth in territories I had never been in before, as I desperately gabbled on about any trivial matter that came into my head. The ashen sky seemed to match the mood inside the café. Raindrops began to fall: first a light drizzle, then a heavy pitter-patter. Finally we left, I for the bus stop, she for her car. We hesitated outside the café door, not knowing what to say to one another. Adibah was the first to speak.

'I'm going back to him.'

'What?' I exclaimed, aghast. 'You can't! After all he's done?'

'I haven't lost everything,' she said, trying to smile. 'I still have my faith.'

'How can you still believe, after everything that's happened?' I asked in amazement.

'Whatever has happened was through human error, not religious fault. While I believe, I can still hope . . . and, well, I'll go from there.'

'I've never met anyone like you before,' I said, staring at

her with a new perspective. She smiled a smile that didn't quite reach her eyes and turned to go. For a long time, I stood watching her receding figure, feeling a deep sadness as the rain trickled down the back of my neck, before I turned to go in the opposite direction.

I never saw Adibah again. In the eight months since I last saw her, I gather she has left her husband and has been touring and lecturing at mosques over the country. I realise now I need never have worried for her; she has an inner strength which few people can boast of, and which, although it is based on beliefs I would question, I can only admire for the lesson it taught me in patience and tolerance, and for its very durability.

Noushin Sorayyapour (11)

*Solitude

Tears come out of her head,
Thoughts flow out of her eyes.
You can see that she feels like
Sitting under a table,
Hitting her arms
So that she can't wipe her tears
From her head.
Her eyes gradually turn purple
From being so lonely.

Suddenly she becomes known.
She stops crying
And stares into the eyes of that person,
And says
With a nervous feeling,
'Go away.'

Sarah Mulvey (16)

*Boarding School – Two Generation Tennis

They come in car-loads, greeting part-time children
With painted smiles; there is little love
Beneath the made-up faces,
No chance to thrive across the physical miles.
And we, the privileged, are left
With what their money can buy:
A private education, and holidays abroad –
And Sunday afternoon polite conversation;
Glimpses of a real world.
They are the sometime parents;
Weekends are Adopt-a-Daddy days.
They come with gifts, to sit,
Or play tennis; or the greater game
Of Happy Families.
But the relief in the goodbyes
Is all too clear; is that guilt
Behind the stony gaze; or is it fear?
Do they realise that they have grown
Not only alien to the goodnight kiss
But from those they call their own?
And when, with brief embrace
And un-met eyes, they leave us here;
I wonder, when they turn away
If there is a conscience in that tear?

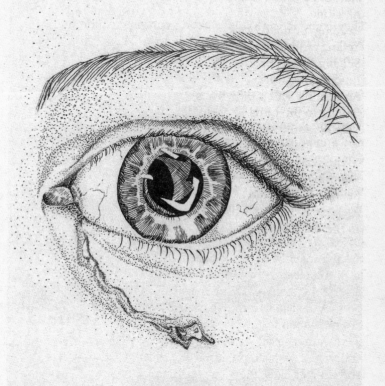

IS THERE A CONSCIENCE IN THAT TEAR?

Diana Blakeney (16)

Marysia Cywinski (8)

*Marooned

Marooned on an island
All alone
Reading a ruined book
Yelling at the boats that pass by
Singing to myself
Ignoring the noise
And eating stale sandwiches
Calling to the birds
Yelping at the sting that the nettles bring
Wading in the water
In the warm sun
Nattering at the animals
Sinking in the sand
Kicking at the shells
In the deep blue sea.

Marysia Cywinski (8)

David Tallach (16)

*The Wall

She seemed to come to life on that day in late August when I was on the road delivering papers, with my small racing bike, my U2 T-shirt and the pale jeans I'd bought only three months ago, my first pair.

She and two or three of her friends were walking along the pavement to my right, and she raised a hand in a friendly gesture that brought my world crashing down around me.

I waved back and speeded round the corner on my bike, unaccustomed as I was to such things happening, and I pondered on the question of her suitability for me as a closer friend than she already was, or her 'compatibility', a word which a boy I knew had used once in similar circumstances, over a computer game later that day.

Strangely, the game was called 'Head Over Heels', which is how I ended up shortly afterwards.

At least, she came alive for me at that moment because she was away from the school and about fifteen metres away from my house, and seeing her there broke the routine, made her more than the character I had known offhand since first year.

Anyway, it was on the morning of Wednesday, thirteenth September 1989, during the third period probably around half past ten, when I made the move that changed everything between her and me, which has affected me severely ever since.

All I did was to look at her, to gaze into her blue-green eyes from across the room with an intensity lacking in any glances I had previously thrown her.

And she was startled, caught unawares, looking back at me after I had looked away, then she looked away too, without smiling.

And I felt like panicking, although no one in the whole room was affected by this incident apart from me: I was shocked and dazed by the abrupt change in my relations with the girl, it came so suddenly, and I didn't really know what I was doing.

On about three occasions afterwards I met her while walking home from school, and she gave me a brilliant, dazzling smile, more beautiful than anything else I have ever seen. And I smiled back and tried to reassure myself, it's all right, she isn't slipping away from me in an icy fog of detachment that I've created.

And this is a novel kind of crisis for me: I am afraid of what I have done to separate her from me in a gesture that was meant to do the opposite.

And I go red and feel shaky whenever she's around, and I can't look her in the face without trembling enough to lose my head. Well, I have lost my head anyway.

It's as if the end of the world has come, as if an iron curtain has come down between us; an impenetrable wall has sprung up for me just as the Berlin Wall is torn down. My life tipped sideways at that point and everything seemed to go mad: it was as if the Red Revolution of 1917 Russia, which we were studying in the history classroom where I had the upset with the girl, was being re-enacted in my life: as if it had come back, with its gory hands, especially for me.

I am more settled now, although less happy, than I was then, although it is a painful thorn in my side that I have never really talked to that girl, never explained, never made my peace with her. If only I could talk. But perhaps I never will.

Avril Huston (15)

*Café Noir

Closing my eyes, I can still see you
Stepping between the chairs and trays
Of the café we always met in,
Holding the proffered coffee, smiling.
It would be black, I knew, hot and sweet,
Overwhelming my senses as I sipped. Its own
Peculiar scent, allied perhaps with yours,
Its taste, and most of all your face, all
Joined together, I could not concentrate.
Thus I lost the best of our few hours
Together. Today I drink tea in the caff, alone,
No longer with you, you who took my address
But would not give me yours, whose home I knew
Only from photographs, unwillingly shown,
No code for reaching you given. I should have known
I would find an empty cup, when I arrived,
With the note folded neatly, underneath the
Saucer, the polite apology, the valediction.
But that was always the difference between us:
You would be subtle, underhand, your French never seemed
Pretentious – 'Café noir', our little secret. And I
Would rather call a cup a cup, call coffee coffee,
Not 'quite the young sophisticate' my mother guessed at,
When she found the bill for two coffees.

Avril Huston (15)

Nicola Smithies (14)

Leaving

As I stood before the small mirror in the dark, damp and shabby bathroom of the rented flat that I'd called 'home' for the last six months of my life, a tear came to my eye. I looked into the chipped and stained surface of the looking glass that hung on the wall by a limp piece of string and I saw a reflection that I hardly recognised.

The face that looked back at me was pale with blotchy tear-stains running down the cheeks. The eyes were not unlike those of a panda. There was a distinct grey bag beneath each eye that looked like a dead weight. It looked even more so with the remains of some black eye makeup that had probably run because of the tears. The face looked tired and blank. The hair surrounding the face looked limp and tatty and very much in need of a wash. In fact the whole face needed a good clean up. I only knew for sure that it was me because when I blinked, so did the image in the mirror.

In an attempt to disguise some of the blankness from my face, I ran the water into the chipped porcelain sink. It was only lukewarm but it was going to have to do. I bent over the basin and reached out and took the small bar of soap from the dish on the side of the cold white basin. I scrubbed my face with my hands using the soap and rinsed it off in the water. I felt better for doing that and then I decided to at least rinse my hair. It had been over a week since I last washed it, I'd never left it that long before.

I dunked my hair into the now soapy water and as I was lifting my head from the basin, a bottle of shampoo on the window ledge caught my eye. I picked it up and with my hair dripping all over the floor, I twisted open the lid and poured some silvery blue shampoo on to the palm of my hand. I flicked my hair back over the basin and started to rub the shampoo into my hair. I worked up a lather and then rinsed it off in the already soapy water. To get the remains of the lathered shampoo out I rinsed my still soap-sudded hair under the tap. The last of the shampoo was washed away with the nearly cold water.

I picked up the small towel from the cold, turned-off radiator. We couldn't afford to have it on until it was really cold, freezing even. I towel-dried my hair in front of the mirror and felt the damp hair on the back of my neck. I felt much better for having washed my face and hair, but I was still determined to go through with it.

'It' was leaving. I'd decided about a week ago to go. I felt I had to get out. I needed to get out. I was going to go to Newcastle, to where I grew up. I had it all planned. I'd stay with my Aunt Jane, who lived just outside the city. She had never married and had always appreciated the company. I was going to try to get a job in the city. I know that I could get quite a good job if I tried, one with prospects. I had some good qualifications, including three 'A' levels and I had done half of a degree in History at Dundee University, before I'd given it all in to live in the small flat in South London, with him. If I were to finish my degree, I know for certain that I could get a good job. I decided that I'd have to see how things went, before I could go and finish my university degree. They were my hopes and plans for the future. I knew that I had a long way to go before I could achieve any of them. Firstly, I had to leave him.

'Him' was otherwise known as Michael. My boyfriend, flat-mate or lover if you like. We'd met at a party, about eighteen months ago. I was on holiday from university at the time. We'd started going out together but before long I was back at university. We wrote to each other and saw each other in the holidays and sometimes at weekends. It was about eight months, in March, that I'd decided to put university 'on hold' for a while to go and be with Michael. We rented a flat in South London, not far from Hammersmith Bridge, and had lived there ever since. He worked as an apprentice plasterer and I'd got a job as a typist in an office in Hammersmith. We were happy – for a while.

Now we seemed to argue all the time over silly little things. He'd always go out for a drink and leave me in the cold and empty flat alone. It was the same routine, day in, day out. The magic seemed to have disappeared from our relationship. I had to get out. I'd wasted enough of my life on him already as it was. I had to get out as quickly as possible, if not sooner. And now I was on the brink of getting out.

My hair was still wet, but not soaking as it had been before. I wrapped the towel round my head and proceeded to wash the rest of my body in the lukewarm water.

After I had finished, I let the now cold water drain away down the plug-hole. I shivered as I put on the clothes that had hung over the back of a wooden chair. I dressed hurriedly in my jeans and a thick jumper so as not to get too cold. I pulled some socks on to my feet and put on my sturdy black shoes. I picked up my rucksack and into it I placed the carefully folded clothes from the wardrobe in the bedroom and some wash things from the bathroom. In the pockets down the sides I put my Walkman and some of my treasured possessions. I put on my well-worn ski jacket and scarf and I put my purse and keys into the pocket of my jeans. I carried my bulging rucksack and put it down in the hallway by the door.

I went into the small shabby-looking kitchen and fumbled about in the half light looking for some paper and a pen. I found a piece of plain white paper and an old blue biro which had had its end chewed off. I scribbled on the corner of the paper to get the ink flowing. Then I began to write my letter.

After I'd finished it I placed the pen back where I'd found it and, clutching the folded piece of paper, I went back to the hallway. I paused by the bedroom door, where I knew he was sleeping. I could hear the rise and fall of his breath as I stood watching him. I moved towards him silently, still clutching the letter tightly in my hand. I dared not make a sound just in case I woke him. His face looked so calm and peaceful. For a moment I wondered why I was leaving. I looked down and saw the letter still in my clenched fist and it reinforced my reasons for leaving.

I felt a tear forming in the corner of my eye as I leaned forward to touch his hair. I caught sight of a photograph by the side of the bed. It was of him and I, taken before we moved in together. He'd had it framed and treasured it dearly.

I felt the tears welling up in my eyes and I unclenched my fist and propped the now creased letter up against the photograph. Slowly I turned and walked towards the door.

Just before I reached the door to the hallway I saw my black felt hat, hanging on a hook on the wall. I loved that hat, I couldn't leave without it. With my eyes filling up with tears I reached out my cold pale hand and gently lifted the hat from the hook on the wall. With a reminiscent smile I put the black felt hat on my head.

As I turned to take one final look at the man who I'd given up my life for until now, I felt the first tear roll down my cheek. So before many more followed it, I wiped it away and with one parting glance I went out into the hallway again. I picked up my rucksack from where I'd left it in the hallway and made my way towards the door.

As quietly as I could, I turned the latch on the front door and stepped out of the flat on to the cold concrete landing of the five-storey tower block. Gently, I closed the door behind me and made my way down the cold concrete stairs with the equally cold metal handrail running alongside them. I reached the bottom of the stairs and as quickly as I could, so as not to disturb anybody, I opened the outside door of the tower block. The murky staircase was lit up by the light from the lamp post outside which, although it was daylight outside, was still on. I stepped outside the tower block into the world that was just waking up. I had enough money in my purse for the train fare from Paddington to Newcastle and some extra just in case I needed it.

I jogged down the steps in front of the flats and on to the pavement. It was about a five-minute walk to the tube station. I got there and bought my ticket. I had to take three different tube trains before I reached my premier destination, Paddington Station.

I arrived at Paddington at 7.45 a.m. My train to Newcastle wasn't due to leave until 8 o'clock, but it was in the station preparing to leave. I bought my ticket and leisurely walked across the station towards my train. I was glad that I'd brought a book from the flat with me. I didn't want to have to spend my money on entertainments such as magazines.

I found an empty compartment in the end carriage. I sat down and began to read. Not long afterwards, at exactly 8 o'clock, the guard blew his whistle and the train pulled out of the station. The journey was to take about four hours and that was the 'express' train as they called it.

For the first hour and a half I was alone in the compartment. Then at a stop in the Birmingham area a young man, dressed in a suit and carrying a smart black briefcase, came into the compartment and sat on the opposite side from me. Not long after he'd sat down, my eyes felt heavy and my whole body felt weary. I soon dropped off to sleep and I must have slept for a long time because when I woke up we were stationary in Newcastle Station. I stood up, stretched and grabbed my bag from under the seat. I let myself out of the carriage on to the platform. It was 12.36 p.m. and I was hungry. I hadn't eaten since yesterday. I found a coffee shop not far from the station and went in. I ordered a coffee and a cheese and pickle sandwich. I ate it, pondering on what I should do next. I could either go to my aunt's house or look around the city. I decided to take a look around the city, to see how much it'd changed in recent years.

I swung my rucksack over my shoulder and went to

explore Newcastle. I went to the Metrocentre and looked in almost every shop there was. I was fascinated by the water-falls and cascades in and amongst the shops. I wandered around the promenades and malls of shops, full of goods from fruit and vegetables to frilly babies' nappies.

At 4.15 p.m. I decided to head off for Aunt Jane's house. She lived on the south side of the city. I took the all too familiar Newcastle train service to about a five-minute walking distance from Aunt Jane's house. I arrived at Aunt Jane's just before it started to go dark. I rang her doorbell and she scuttled to answer it. She was surprised to see me. Amazed would be a better word.

Aunt Jane was a survivor. She'd coped on her own for all these years. She knew just what I needed after such a long day. She, herself, had travelled all over Asia when she was younger so my journey was hardly a walk in the park compared to her expeditions.

She sat me down in the warm and cosy kitchen and brewed a pot of tea. I remembered when I was a child Aunt Jane had always had a pot of tea just brewing. I sat in the varnished wooden chair with its soft cushion and just relaxed. She made me my favourite sandwich, chicken and mushroom, and sat down opposite me at the table.

'So,' she said as I tucked into my sandwich, 'what are you doing all the way up here?'

'I'm going to stay here, if that's all right with you, of course. I want to make my life up here now,' I told her.

'I thought you were living with that boy, Michael?'

'I was.'

'Oh, what happened?'

So I told her the whole story from start to finish and she listened attentively.

'Very admirable, my dear,' she said after a moment's silence, 'especially the ideas about the job.'

Aunt Jane had always been one for practicality.

'Of course you can stay here, with plans like that I'd be

glad to help out,' she told me. 'I'm glad you've got that young ruffian out of your life,' she added.

The 'young ruffian' had found the letter. He'd woken up just before 7.30 a.m. He thought she'd got up and gone into the kitchen. He saw the letter, still propped up against the photograph, when he rolled over to see the time. He propped himself up in bed and unfolded the creased white paper. He began to read it slowly.

When he'd finished he got out of bed and went to the wardrobe. He looked on the shelves and in the drawers to see if she'd taken much stuff with her, to see if she really had gone. And she had. Her jacket was missing from behind the door and most of her clothes were gone too. She really had gone.

He read the letter again, searching for any trace of where she might have gone. He found none. He pulled on his worn maroon dressing gown and hurriedly dashed round the flat looking for traces of Rachael, signs to say she'd been there. He found only what he knew was there, the bathroom, the kitchen, the living room, but no Rachael.

He went back to bed, hoping he'd wake up to find it had all been a bad dream, that Rachael was still there, but he didn't. He hoped that maybe she'd come back, have a change of heart. But she didn't.

At Aunt Jane's house I was unpacking in the small back bedroom that Aunt Jane had told me I could have as my room. Out of the window I could see the city of Newcastle in lights. It was a beautiful sight. The street lamps scattered all over, like a giant dot-to-dot puzzle, lit up the waters of the Tyne. It was a breathtaking view and I could just imagine being on the banks of the Tyne, with all the lights lighting up the sky.

'Rachael!' Aunt Jane called up the stairs, 'will you come down for a minute.' That wasn't a question, more of an order.

I distracted myself from the view and pulled the curtains

before going downstairs. When I got downstairs I found Aunt Jane in the kitchen. She'd made a pot of tea and a chicken casserole was cooking on the stove.

'Sit down, love,' she said gently. 'You know before when I said that Michael was a "young ruffian"?'

'Yes,' I said, pulling out a chair from beneath the table.

'Well, I didn't mean it quite like that.'

'Oh!'

'Well, he'll have feelings too, won't he?' she said, and not waiting for an answer she went on, 'So maybe you should let him know you're safe.'

I'd thought for one moment that she was saying that I should go back to him.

'Yes, I suppose I ought to,' I said quietly.

'I suggest that you phone him now,' she said, her mind quite made up.

'Where would I get hold of him?' I asked. We hadn't had a phone. If we ever wanted to call anyone we'd gone to the phone box down the road, and incoming calls were virtually non-existent. I decided to ring Tony and Gillian. They lived across the landing from us and they had a phone.

So I did.

I dialled the number carefully, 081-641 8937, after several rings it was answered.

'Hello, Gillian Barton speaking,' said the voice at the other end of the receiver.

'Hello, Gill,' I said, 'it's me, Rachael.'

'Rachael!' she exclaimed. 'Where are you? Michael's gone crazy!'

'I'm at my aunt's. Could you get Michael, please? I'd like to speak to him if that's okay.'

'Sure,' she replied, 'I'll see if he's in, one moment.'

Gillian went away and I heard her knocking at the front door of my old home. A few moments later, someone picked up the receiver.

'Rachael?' It was Michael.

'Yeah, it's me. Did you get my letter?'

'Yes. Please, Rach . . . '

I cut him short. 'Michael, don't ask questions, please. Just listen.'

He grunted softly at the other end.

'I'm sorry to have had to leave,' I said, 'I didn't mean to hurt you. If you read the letter you'll understand why I've gone. I'm only phoning to let you know I'm safe and well.' I finished off, 'I'm only phoning to say goodbye. I couldn't say that this morning.'

Michael said nothing.

'Michael, are you there?'

'Yes, I'm here. Can't we just talk about it?' he asked.

'There's nothing to say, nothing that hasn't already been said,' I told him.

'Please, Rachael, just tell me one thing.'

'What?'

'Is it because of my drinking some nights?'

'Some nights!' I retorted. 'Every night! That's partly it, but there were other things too. I was just there when you wanted me. I can't stand being used – and you used me. When you wanted me I had to be there and I was sick of it. You wouldn't listen to me anyway.'

'Come on, Rach! It'll be different now, honest.'

'What do you mean "now"?' I asked him angrily. 'We are through. Ended. Finito. Stopped. Do you hear me? There is no "we" or "us" any more. I've left.'

Michael was silent again.

'So that's it?' he said. 'Just like that, you've gone?'

'Yes. That's the way it is.'

'Oh.' He seemed lost for words.

'So, goodbye, Michael. Best wishes for the future.'

'Yes. And you. Bye,' he said blankly.

'Bye,' I said, hanging up the receiver.

I turned to Aunt Jane who'd come into the room.

'How was he?' she asked.

'Fine,' I said. 'He's just fine.'

'Oh good,' Aunt Jane said, 'now you can get on with your life.'

'Yes,' I said smiling, 'I can.'

And off I went upstairs to finish unpacking and to plan my future on the banks of the Tyne.

Michael sat down in the poorly furnished living area. The letter was on the coffee table in front of him. He was stunned, that was for sure. Slowly he reached out for the plain white piece of paper. Gently he unfolded it and read it.

Dear Michael,

By the time you read this letter I will be far away. I'm sorry to have to do this to you, but there is no other way. I can't go on like this, so I've decided to get out, while I can.

I'm going to make something of my life. I'm going to continue with the plans I had, before I packed them in to be with you. I don't want to go on in this way and end up being stuck here for ever.

Maybe I'll see you again, maybe I won't, but I hope you'll forgive me, I needed to do this for me.

Please don't try to find me, I'll let you know when I've sorted things out somewhere else.

I wish you all the best for your life and the future.

Goodbye.
from
Rachael

This time when he read it, the words sank in whereas before they'd washed over him like a tidal wave on a beach. Now they sank in and he realised what they were saying to him. The letter dropped to the floor and, with his head in his hands, he cried.

* * *

In the bathroom at Aunt Jane's, I stood before the mirror and looked closely at myself. I looked different from this morning and I recognised myself. As I peered into the reflecting glass I saw on my face what had made all the difference – there, in the bathroom, in Aunt Jane's house, my face had a smile on it.

Harriet Margolies (16)

Untitled

Looking out of her window she could see the backs of the houses opposite – big, late-Victorian houses with soot-blackened bricks and ornate plasterwork. At least half were now flats, for yuppie couples with no kids and too much money. This house was still whole, not dismembered like the rest. It was a nice view across the long, green gardens, full of trees in blossom and clean, yellow, wood fences. If she looked out of his window she could see across the city, to the Thames and the dockyards – disused now of course. Behind that, the Isle of Dogs and its huge towerblock, slicing a chunk out of the sky, surrounded by skeletal cranes. She felt sorry for him having his view ruined – he was such an aesthetic person. She was glad now that she had this room.

She crossed to the table and began to clear it, putting the jam-smeared spoon and plate in the sink and giving the grimy surface a perfunctory wipe. Then she cleared the paper from the chair, placed them on a pile of similar dog-eared objects, and sat down. She never threw things out, she couldn't bear to. She was always terrified that one day she'd need something and she'd have thrown it away. So instead she had piles of musty, yellowed newspapers along the walls and trunks of old letters, bits of material, stubs of pencils. Scraps of paper, pens that had run out, dead plants – they all littered her room as if some misguided Womble had been storing their hoard in her room. She couldn't understand why he minded so much – it wasn't as if it was his room.

A slippery thud came faintly from downstairs. The post had arrived. She shoved her veiny feet into her shabby slippers and thumped downstairs and excitedly grabbed the three thin envelopes lying on the cold tiles. All for him. Disappointed, she dropped them and slowly dragged herself upstairs again. She turned on the radio, expecting to hear the calming, mind-numbing sounds of Radio 2. Instead her ears were engulfed in a wave of meaningless noise, full blast. Shocked, she turned the radio off again – it was one of his bands, the ones he loved to listen to – just because she hated them.

She abandoned the Judas radio and looked at the clock. Only 12 a.m., she still had another six hours to wait until he came home. She felt so isolated here although she loved the house, it was just being alone all day she didn't like. She didn't really know anyone round here, he didn't like it when she talked to other people. It was such a difference here to where she'd lived before. There the houses were smaller, overflowing with loud, cheerful families, whose self-absorbed chatter and expansive arguments surrounded, but did not involve her. She'd liked that, being an onlooker. Here there was nothing to watch. Middle-class housewives left their neatly painted, neutral-coloured doors, and climbed into their conservative blue Volvos, carrying Monet motif shopping bags they'd picked up on their last cultural exped-ition, and drove off.

Hometime was better, at least the small children were more brightly coloured, but they too had a middle-aged reserve that was surprising to her. Instead of garish, rich, totally uncalorie-controlled chocolate bars, they ate healthy muesli snacks and kept the wrappers, instead of blithely dropping them. They talked quietly too, no screaming or yelling. It was so boring.

She turned back to the room, she did hate this waiting. She'd spend all day alone, doing mindless, tiring things that irritated her, or worse nothing at all, until he came home. Then he'd look round, antagonised by the traffic he'd battled through, and berate her for not making the house cleaner or cosier. After that he'd start on her, how she looked too sloppy or too smart, or anything.

It always interested her to watch his face as he yelled at her. It would change colour and twist into horrible shapes and his eyes would begin to bulge. After a while it began to frighten her and occasionally she'd cry. She'd feel her face getting hotter and her eyes beginning to ache and then the thin trail of salty water would drip down her face and spatter her clothes. She was all right as long as he didn't see, but if he did it'd be even worse.

He threw a teapot at her once; it hadn't hit her, but it had scared her. She'd never realised he'd had that much anger stored up. She could imagine it, boiling away, scalding hot, acidic, scraping away at his brain with its foul purplish liquid, until it escaped.

She didn't think he realised how much hate he had either, the look on his face after he'd thrown the teapot was incredulous. Since then, though, he'd got worse, realising he could do almost anything now.

A few years ago, when she was braver, she'd started to take pottery classes. They'd been fun, an escape from the absolute boredom of the house, and she'd been able to talk to people, without his control. He hated it, even though he'd often complained about how she mooched around the house. After a while she gave up, she couldn't stand the fierce black looks and furious mutterings when she returned, exultant, red-cheeked from the fresh air. She'd done nothing like it since.

Glancing at the clock, it was 1.30 at last. She could have lunch now, relieve the boredom. She opened the fridge and removed a small block of yellowish, cracked cheese of dubious age and an almost empty pint of milk, just past the sell-by date. These she put carefully on a corner of the table. Then she took a small cup, plate and knife out of the drainer. Lastly, she took the loaf of bread off the top of the fridge and placed that too on the table. Slowly she cut a wafer-thin slice of the cheese and put it on the slice of bread and half filled the cup with the milk, topping it up with water. Then she began to eat.

He'd said she was fat, that she should go on a diet. So this was what she had for lunch. He placed no restriction on how much she could eat at once, but this had to last the rest of the week, so she had little choice.

Supper was better, he had to eat it too, so they had real food, just she had much less. He wouldn't let her shop any more, she had to write a list every morning and he bought it. He didn't like having to do it, but it was his own decision. When she cooked, she would eat little bits when he was out of the room. Still, she got much less hungry these days.

When she finished, she cleared away. She couldn't decide what was worse: waiting for him, or him being there. It was better than living alone, that would have driven her mad, she just needed a reassuring presence, that she was safe. Not that, with his increasing fits of anger, he could really be called very safe, but better than facing the world. At least his violence was known to her, predictable.

She used to be much braver, much more willing to confront him. He'd always been stronger, more dominant, since they were small, but then at least she fought back, even if she lost. Now the thought of arguing with him was so alien, it was almost laughable. She hated herself for being so weak but it was too late now, what could she do? She felt like an amoeba, barely alive, just existing with no real capacity for thought or anything, not any more.

She'd left once, gone away, left a note explaining, but she'd had to come back. She'd gone back to where she'd lived as a student, before the breakdown that caused her to move in with him. It wasn't like it had been then. When she'd lived there, they'd spend afternoons lying on the rough green lawns of the local park, laughing and being sometimes silly, sometimes philosophical. The town had been beautiful, with houses from five different eras all crammed together on one narrow street. Little parks were dotted all over town and you could spend all afternoon in pubs or tea rooms, with low ceilings and cramped tables.

When she'd gone back to find her old haunts, they'd all changed or gone. The parks were full of drunken louts and angry mothers with whingeing children, and the grass was covered in rubbish, benches destroyed. They'd rebuilt the town centre. It was full of blank, characterless glass shopping centres and office blocks. A choice of pubs full of Karaoke machines or Wimpy bars.

She didn't dare go and see the houses she'd lived in, the street she'd loved. Instead she'd wandered demoralised round the town until, crying angrily at the state she was in, she went home. When she got back, he hit her, not hard, but she had a panic attack and locked herself in her room for two days. After that her courage was totally gone, she didn't even contemplate doing it again, despite the fact things had got worse. It was going back that had done it, if she'd gone somewhere new she could have managed, she wouldn't have felt that absolute despair at everything being different. Well it was too late now, she was stuck with this life.

She slowly got up and began to wipe down the table, in preparation for her brother coming down. The yellow cloth dragged across the rough surface and the sticky patches. She put the cloth down and began very gently to cry, long low gasps and sobs, going on and on. She wondered if she'd ever be able to stop. She caught sight of the clock, 5.45! He'd be home soon. She sniffed, wiped her eyes, and sat, waiting.

Waiting, as she always did, for him to come home.

Rachel Armstrong (16)

**Brother

She can feel his movement
warm through the wall.
Picture him,
like an infra-red camera;
clammy cheek cold on bluish
white porcelain.
Eyes, fixed wet, on the vomit-fringed plughole.

Silence clings like parachute silk.
Her pulse throbs dully in stretched tight wrists.
The moon hangs silver and he
will not look at the clock; it is of no interest
to catch him in a lie any more.

Ten a.m.; his eyes are purple-smudged shadows,
hair limp like a blind. Lips dry and
nervous as he slumps in the car,
juggling questions from his parents with sweating palms,

And glances uneasily across at the
one weak point in his fabrication
who gazes intently at the round horizon,
clocking each receding pylon through blurring tears.

Louise Hughes (16)

Malcolm Smith (16)

Rebecca Goss (16)

**Tuesday before Easter

Our house was damp and the mould
Spread down our walls, staining the paper.
Mother sighed, fingers sticky with sugar,
Sweets were part of her religion.
Father sighed, wouldn't move not even potter.
Depression was part of his neurosis.

It made conversation, the illness, the neurosis,
So did the pictures, hung to hide our mould.
They were designed by the local potter,
'A real Artist,' said Mother, sucking rice paper,
'And a worshipper too.' It was important to her – her
    religion.
She filled up her guests' cups and offered them all sugar.

Father spilt the bowl of sugar.
He cried, it's his neurosis.
Mother comforted, oozed religion.
Sat him in his chair, his back to the mould
And gave him his daily paper.
The local potter arrived, Mother beamed 'Oh, Potter!'

Soon after I was alone with Potter.
He said he liked my dress, said I was as sweet as sugar,
Wrote down 'pulchritudinous' on a piece of paper,
Said I was me, I didn't have neurosis.
He said my body he would mould.
That evangelical bastard, that religion.

I bathed, as mother read from her book of religion.
Pulled my head beneath the water, rinsed the smell of Potter.

Mother dressed me for school and I leant against the mould
While she sang and put her cornflakes with my sugar.
'I'll never get neurosis'
Mother hissed and hit me with the paper.

Wasn't allowed to mention it in front of father, his paper
Blocking everything out anyway, including the religion.
My father didn't deserve neurosis.
Only one man did, I watched that Potter potter
Across to my mother, giving sugar.
Later his clay-stained hands would push me up against the
    mould.

I never took religion, and it was Potter
Who took me, he gave messages on paper and gave sugar
But he took me, when my father had neurosis and our walls
    had mould.

IN A BIG BAD BACK YARD

Glen Rust (11)

Helena Echlin (15)

*Untitled

I never wanted
to have a baby,
growing like a fungus,
invading my body space.

Floating bag
of cellophane and skin,
flesh bud
in my womb.

I never liked that picture,
the one in the text book,
of a prawn-coloured embryo
with raisin eyes,
tadpole head.

Your hands and feet
are still flesh flippers,
but I love your delicate
light bulb skull
and that look you have
of intense concentration.

It's much too squashed
this jelly baby
and I don't like
its plasticine face,
I don't like its thumbnail smile.

Little astronaut
with your blank peaceful face
attached to the moon
by the umbilical cord.

Katy Knight (16)

It is thin as a Jew
from a concentration camp,
its head is furred with mucus
and its eyes are dead
and distant as fossils.

I can see your hands now,
your starfish hands.

A pregnant woman
loses her identity,
becoming nothing more
than a gross container.
A pregnant woman is an egg on legs.
How can she bear her ballooning womb?

Your skin is pale as mushroom,
your face is ancient, tender.

I don't like not knowing
what it will be like,
it could be Einstein,
it could be Hitler
and there aren't any refunds,
nowhere to take it back to.

Finally
the terrible
birth like an animal,
you're ripped open,
you're inside out
for a baby born peeled
like a runover fruit.

They wash the thing,
they put it in my arms
but I don't recognise it,
is this mine?
Did I produce
this changeling child?

The infant's face
is a thousand years old,
it won't milksick
but utter prophecies
and the infant's smile
is a Buddha smile.
'It's not mine,' I want to scream.
'Take it back, TAKE IT BACK.'

Michelle Gallen (14)

No Place Like Home

Dublin airport is always cold. It seems bare and unwelcoming, even if you have tearful relatives rejoicing in your return. It's colder still if you have just come from the late summer heat of New York, and no relatives, tearful or otherwise, come to greet you. After ten years, ten birthdays, ten Christmasses from home, you would like someone, anyone. Instead, I now have to face Ireland alone for a while.

I am going by bus to meet someone. A lady who helped me a lot, just before I was able to leave Ireland. She welcomes me, resuming the mother rôle. This lady has had so many rôles to play in her life, as I have had. Neither of us has ever been on stage. She sets the Irish bacon, cabbage and potatoes in front of me, and the taste is wonderful. The conversation is casual, it is of the next house to visit, where to find the car. She gives me some money and I leave.

Ireland hasn't changed in ten years. The rain is as cold, the people as warm, and the North as divided. I arrive at the next house, they are expecting me. I am told to stay the night, then my next contact is in Tyrone. I sleep in Ireland for the first time in ten years.

I wait at the border crossing. The light flashes green, just for a fraction of a second. I manoeuvre the car around the numerous concrete blocks, designed for the soldiers' safety. So much more permanent than ten years ago. My licence is asked for by a soldier, with green and black 'make-up' as we used to call it, smeared over his young face. He holds a black gun in one hand, the other is held out for my licence. Questions being asked. Jet-lag is making me sleepy, don't become confused. The old hate is still there, stronger even. Absence makes the heart grow fonder. British accents reading my number plate. The soldier can't place my accent, so tries to get me to talk a little more. He smiles as he hands back my licence. I remain blank. A woman can get away with more, a young man would have been stopped, searched, into an argument by now. I accelerate into Tyrone.

I arrive at my next house with no trouble. More danger up here, more danger of recognition. I have one day to myself, to travel, meet friends. I see many, and talk of old times. Some are now dead, or in prison, but I know of these already. My accent is preserved, still Irish, but not as easy in speaking or localised. You would know I am Irish, but no more. America did that to me. Many Irish there, all different, but all the same in one way. My fund-raising there wasn't for charity.

I go to Saturday night mass, more sombre, more restrained than the American celebration. I find it depressing. Old women's toothless mutterings distract me from my thoughts. The priests' words lull me away from reality, like hypnotism. Is that what religion really is? Mass hypnotism? Prayers finished and the final blessing received, I go out with the rest of the congregation, only to retreat back into the chapel as I find an army patrol, passing 'co-incidentally'. I leave when all is silent.

Today, I meet friends again. These are friends I never lost contact with. We meet in a pub, anonymous and friendly. We laugh easily, and talk tough. The Northern accent is much harder than the Southern one, giving words a viciousness you only notice when foreign. After they leave, I stay in the smoky security of the pub, thinking.

It's not easy deciding whether or not to visit a family who were once close to you, but haven't been in contact with you for ten years. I went. I regretted it. In your memory, faces are soft, blurred. Ten years of living leave an indelible line. It was strange to sit down once more to dinner with my family. But they are no longer my family. I was treated with an unbearable politeness, and they called me by my full name, not my old family name. I didn't expect a prodigal daughter act, but it still hurt. Time doesn't heal all things, some situations get worse, as mine did. But everyone suffers for their beliefs, I suppose. Time hasn't healed Northern Ireland's problems either – they've got worse, the walls higher and thicker, the people growing more narrow-minded.

I used to dream of dying heroically in a hail of bullets, I wanted to be shot down in flames. I wanted to be part of history. Some chance I had in a remote troubled part of Tyrone, where the careers officer advised factory jobs, or training schemes, and that if you stated your nationality as British, you were more likely to get a job. I was in intelligence, what with women's guiles, hand in hand with guns, and a flair for mechanics and precision. My teachers had deemed me bright, and my parents had always expected something different of me. They were a middle-class, SDLP-voting family, respectable and hard working. Always one black sheep I suppose.

I've always been Irish, read Irish books – of IRA heroes and heroines against the mighty British forces, dying for their country. I suppose I became convinced through them. That and seeing my parents having to grovel to soldiers with the IQ of your average Irish sheep, but not half the manners. When I refused to do as they did, harassments, dreading the red light in the middle of the road, signalling the presence of a patrol in the dead of night. When I was asked, I didn't refuse.

It's a wonder my parents didn't suspect, ever. I went to Germany for a year, travelled Libya, America. They thought it was my training for mechanics, naturally a woman has to travel more for her training – it's all experience anyway – sure Germany leads the world in mechanics. Unfortunate about the few bombs that went off during my stay – surely you'd expect a break from all that, it being a foreign country and all. I don't think they'd know today, if it hadn't been for that misfortune ten and a half years ago.

I did go out on a few missions, but mostly I just planned them, or tried to build better bombs out of ordinary unsuspicious items. I was very successful. But something always has to go wrong. On a border scouting mission we literally bumped into a patrol. We didn't panic, but when you're carrying guns, ammunition and a grenade or two, you don't want to be searched. We opened fire, and escaped into County Donegal. We lost one man that night, the Brits lost four. I don't remember very much about that night, only that the shooting went on for ages, and it was too dark to see who or what you were shooting at. I got wounded in the arm, but didn't realise until afterwards.

That was the end of my home life. It isn't that hard to figure out who's a terrorist from a bullet wound and a passport, you can't do everything with false papers. I stayed down South, moving from safe house to safe house, until my flight to America was arranged. I got on well there, but managed to keep a low profile. Now I'm back. I can move through Northern Ireland with precautions. But that's not how I want to live.

I reckon women always have more to prove, if involved. I think we become more hardened than men, even more dedicated. I have made a decision, and shall put it to my comrades tonight.

This is the last drive anywhere I shall ever make. This is how I want to go, how I've always wanted to go. I've made a few arrangements, no famous last words, just arrangements on my death. I am wired to two and a half tonnes of explosives. The van is creaking under its weight. I am driving towards an RUC barracks. Inside, soldiers sleep. Policemen watch the flickering monitors. Taps drip. The gates open for me.

Alexander Sloan (16)

The Hobby

'I heard a rumour,' Sangstrom said, 'to the effect that you— ' He turned his head and looked around to make sure that he and the chemist were alone in the tiny prescription pharmacy. The chemist was a gnomelike, gnarled little man who could have been any age from fifty to eighty. They were alone, but Sangstrom lowered his voice anyway. ' —to the effect that you have a completely undetectable poison.'

The chemist nodded. He came around the counter and locked the front door of the shop. 'I was about to take a coffee break,' he said. 'Come and have a cup with me.'

Sangstrom followed him into a back room ringed by shelves of bottles from floor to ceiling. The chemist plugged in a coffee percolator and sat down at a small table. He motioned for Sangstrom to do the same. 'Now,' he said. 'Tell me. Whom do you want to kill, and why?'

'Does it matter?' Sangstrom asked. 'Isn't it enough that I pay for— '

'Yes, it matters,' interrupted the chemist with an upraised hand. 'I must be convinced that you deserve what I can give you. Otherwise . . . ' He shrugged, leaving the statement hanging in the air.

'All right, all right,' Sangstrom said. 'The whom is my wife. The why, well . . . ' He started the long story and, towards the end, he was briefly interrupted while the chemist got the coffee. Sangstrom finished his story.

The chemist nodded. 'After hearing your story, I think that you deserve the poison.'

'Fine,' Sangstrom said, 'please give it to me then.'

The chemist smiled mirthlessly at him. 'I already have. It was in your coffee. The poison itself is freely given, but there is a price for the antidote.'

Sangstrom looked down into his empty cup and turned pale. He pulled a pistol from his pocket.

This time the chemist laughed outright. 'You daren't use that. Can you possibly find the antidote amongst all these bottles? Or would you instead find a faster, more virulent poison? Or perhaps you think I'm bluffing? Maybe I am. You'll find out in three hours when the poison starts to act.'

'How much for the antidote?' growled Sangstrom as he lowered his pistol.

'Quite reasonable. A thousand pounds. After all, a man must live. Even if his hobby is preventing murders, there's no reason why he shouldn't make a profit out of it, is there? And another thing, for your wife's safety and mine – you will write a letter confessing of your intention, your former intention, I trust, to kill your wife. Then you will wait here while I go and send it to a friend of mine at Scotland Yard. He'll keep it as evidence in case you ever decide to kill your wife, or me for that matter.

'When I return I will give you the antidote. Oh, and just one more thing. Please help spread the word about my undetectable poison. You never know, the life you save may just be your own.'

Emma Forrest (14)

*Where the Demon Waits

If only you'd concentrate,
You could go far.

How far?
As far as the corner shop?
As far as the moon?
Or somewhere in between?

That's the place I'm most scared of,
That's where I don't want to be.

Alexander Sloan (16)

Beat the Devil

Walter Hill was having problems. Head of Mathematics at Harvard, and still he was having problems. He just couldn't figure out this equation. It infuriated him. He'd been over every formula out loud and did his normal working on a board. He'd gotten it down to the last section, now all he needed was the final breakthrough, but, try as he did, he couldn't get it.

'Damn!' He swore loudly. 'I'd sell my soul for an answer to this.'

'Done,' answered a smug voice from the back of the class-room.

Walter turned around to see a young, muscular man wearing black jeans, black leather boots and a bright red T-shirt with a slogan saying 'Let's Do Armageddon' on it. The man had a satisfied grin on his face. The smile widened as he removed his dark sunglasses to reveal a pair of burning red eyes.

'Do you want to go now, or take the test first?'

Walter was dumbfounded. After a while he recovered his senses sufficiently to ask, 'Do you go after every poor guy who says that?'

'You bet,' came back the reply. The grin widened another notch.

'But it was just a slip of the tongue. I didn't mean it!'

'Hey, man! Don't forget who you're dealing with here, okay. I'm the Devil. You know, evil, the bad guy. Besides, those equations you were saying, they make a pretty hot demonic incantation.'

'But that's not fair,' Walter managed to gasp.

'Of course it isn't. I'm the Devil. I'm not a fair guy.'

'Anyway, what do you want my soul for?' asked Walter.

'Man, are you behind! We sell them, baby. You know, for money.'

'But who to?' asked Walter, puzzled.

'To people in other dimensions. I can just see yours now. You'd go to a planet full of numbers. You'd probably start out as a fraction. Who knows, you may even make it to an integer!'

This shook Walter for a while. When he recovered, he asked, 'You mentioned something about a test?'

'Oh, yeah. This is the fun part. You get to ask me three questions about my psyche and— '

'Your psyche? What's that?'

'Are you totally stupid? My psyche is my power. Anyway,

you get to ask me three questions about my psyche and then you've got to set me a task to perform. I think I should tell you, I've only failed once before, and that was in 1051 BC, so your chances are pretty low, bud.' The smile had now vanished and was replaced by a challenging look, as if daring Walter to try.

'So you're saying that if I set you an impossible task, you'll go and leave me alone?' questioned Walter.

'First question. Yes. Next question?'

'Hey, that's not fair!'

'Walt, baby. We've been through this before, remember. Evil and all that stuff. Fairness isn't one of my strong points.'

Walter's mind was racing now, desperately searching for good, clever questions.

'Is there any limit to your powers?' was what he decided on.

'None. I can do anything. I can travel faster than light, I can make two atoms occupy the same space. I can do anything, anywhere, anytime.' No traces of a smile remained now. He leaned close to Walter threateningly. 'Next question, bud?'

'Is there anywhere that you could go and not find your way back here?' said Walter. A plan was beginning to form in the back of his mind.

The Devil laughed. A harsh, grating, mocking laugh. Walter hoped he'd never hear anything like it again.

'I'm disappointed in you, Walt. I expected more from you. Your answer is no. I can sunbathe in the core of the sun, I can go to the Andromeda system and back in a millisecond, less if I don't stop for lunch.'

He leaned even closer, his face almost touching Walter's. 'Now for the task. Tell me, Walt baby!'

'Not so much a task. More of a command.'

'Lay it on me, bud!'

The moment of truth arrived. Walter said simply and quite calmly, 'Get lost.'

'No!' the Devil screamed and cursed as he was slowly dragged back into his realm. Soon all that was left were his dark glasses. Walter walked over and picked them up. He walked over to a bin and dropped them in.

'Well,' Walt said, 'that one wasn't much help at all.' And at that he turned back to the board and carried on with his work.

Isaac Raine (11)

*The Garage Monster

We had done it for over a year now, ever since we moved to our new house. Every day, just after six, Mum and me would go down to the garage and put our car away. Sometimes Michael comes too.

At winter it gets very dark there, but all year round there are the same sludgy brown leaves and puddles everywhere. There is our garage, and two others, both with enormous corrugated metal doors, which you slide up under the roof when you want to get into the garage.

When I was about five, I always thought that if you knocked three times on the door of our old garage, a witch would come out of the door.

One day, when I was supposed to be doing my maths prep, but reading a book instead, Mum called up for me to go to the garage with her. I hid my book and opened my maths books and put them on my desk. Then I ran downstairs. Mum was there with Michael.

We all got into the car. Michael turned round and started talking to me about the photos of us he'd been looking at.

When we got to the garage, Michael and I got out of the car and scuffled up the leaves. They reminded me of cereal left in milk for too long.

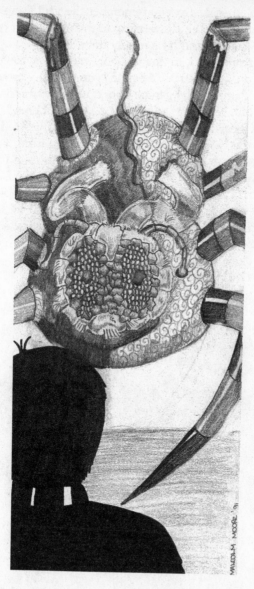

Malcolm Moore (12)

'Michael,' I said. 'Do you remember the wall thing?'

'Mm,' said Michael. He went up to the metal door of one of the other garages and hit it loudly three times.

'Help!' I screamed, in mock terror, pretending to faint.

'Come *on*,' said Mum. 'What are you hanging around for?' Then she slammed the garage doors. We were walking down the lane, Mum in front, and me and Michael behind.

I could hear a damp, heavy 'thudd-d, thudd-d'. I looked round in the direction where it was coming from. I felt nervous, but silly to be feeling nervous. I turned round and carried on walking.

There was a huge shattering crash, and it came out of the garage, feeling its way with its nine segmented legs pawing the ground and its thick see-through hairs waving slightly in the wind.

Michael Clear (12)

116

It had a huge lumpy body mazed with the grooves in a finger-print. At the front it had two legs on each side, both bending out and then in, like a C. When it walked the segments bent, showing brown ooze. Each leg had three or four tooth-brush-bristles coming out from it. In the middle of the body there was one long brown much thinner, longer and more human hair. Its head was bowed and seemed to be joined to the rest of its body by two necks. It had two circular raspberry eyes. It had two antennae which curved out of its eyes like an unfinished semi-circle, and all over its face and eyes were more toothbrush-bristles. Covering its eyes was flaky skin, like the chopped almonds on a cake.

I ran, treading on dog mess, and slipping on leaves. Michael was in front, and I couldn't see Mum any more. When I was little I used to run as fast as I could, pretending someone was chasing me. Now it was totally different. I couldn't run fast at all. I felt like shouting, 'Mum? Where are you? Are you all right?' but I didn't want to draw attention to myself. I looked behind me and saw it lumbering at me fast, not quite getting stuck between the lane's walls. I was nearly home now, and I could hear Michael opening the front door. I got there, stumbling on the pebbled drive, and kicked at our door. Nothing happened.

'Michael! Let me in! Please!'

And the monster churned up the pebbles as it came nearer to the door.

Denise Robinson (8)

*What will she think?

What will she think
if she sees
my big brown eyes?
And what if she sees
my long curly tail
coming out of the bed covers?
(I desire a juicy, tender bite
of little girl.)
What will she think
if she sees
my long, pointed, rubber nose?
(I smell her coming
down the lane.
Blood squirting everywhere
as I bite into her.)
What will she think
if she sees
my big ears coming out of my bonnet?
What will she think
if she sees
my long, pink tongue
hanging out, gasping
for something nice?
She might think
I am her granny
and sit next to me.

James Noble (12)

American Cat in London

Dressed smartly in his fur coat,
The cat is a businessman,
With no guarantee.
The Cat,
With his gas mask face,
Is a dirty dealer.
Cat Capone is back in town.

Steven Ward (12)

The Cat,
Carried away with his short-comings,
Arrested,
Charged,
Imprisoned.

Stephanie Coe (12)

Bail paid and cat walks free.
Cat's eyes stab the dark,
As he strides out of his house,
His coat almost merged into the Victorian
Bricks of the terrace.
His whiskers a moustache,
His claws
Are his pens,
And his mouth, his briefcase.

Georgina Hucker (13)

This cat's ears are Sky Television receivers
as used by his next door neighbour.
The cat is a cat burglar no more.
Yes, the cat is a businessman,
in a big bad back yard.

Tracy Martin (12)

*Gutting a Goose

One misty night my dad goes off with his gun under his arm. He is off to a marsh called the Banana Marsh as it is in the shape of a banana. He hides in the bushes and keeps very quiet until he hears a goose flutter up into the sky. He lifts

Alexander Balls (11)

his gun to his shoulder and takes his aim and fires; he hits the bird in the head and it falls to the ground. THUD! He trundles back to his van along the muddy path. When he gets back he heaves the bird into the back. When he reaches home he says,

'Here you are, Mother,' and hands the bird to my mum.

She replies back by saying,

'Oh brilliant.'

Tom Shiers (11)

Next morning the bird is completely forgotten about until I walk into the kitchen and see it lying there on the work-top. It stares at me with its big beady eyes. Mum comes down having forgotten about it as well and just wanders into the kitchen and she nearly jumps out of her skin. Later that day Mum gets out her bin-bag and starts to take off the feathers. I usually help but I decide to sit and watch instead. The more she plucks, the room fills with more feathers. She tries to put them in the bag but they just fly out again. It looks like a snow scene from the middle of winter. I am asked to clear them up but I just sit still and watch them float to the floor.

Dad comes along with his big knife as soon as Mum has finished plucking off the down (which is used in pillows and duvets). He usually has to ask where about to cut as he never remembers.

First the feet are cut off, then the wing tips, then the head but he leaves some of the neck to make the gravy. A slit is cut across the bottom. There is usually a thick layer of yellow

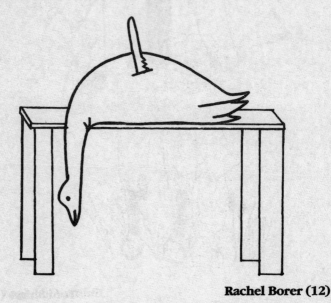

Rachel Borer (12)

124

fat which is round the body as well. When he finds the insides, he starts with the green intestines which he pulls for yards and yards. After this he finds the crop. This is a pinky colour and is very hard. It grinds up the goose's food. The stomach, heart, liver, kidney all come out as one lump. GLOOP! on to the newspaper. We need to save the heart, liver and the part of the neck to make the gravy. Once we've made sure that the bird is cleaned out in the insides we wash it thoroughly before putting it on a tray.

I am usually all right when I watch this. My brother backs off each time it is done. I am usually the one who is made to put the newspaper in the bin. The worst is it stinks of rotten fish. The smell lingers around the house for days after this task is done.

Just think what my dad has gone through just for our Sunday lunch.

Emma Aldridge (11)

William Mair (12)

*Shelter Scene: Bunks and Sleepers

(From the pen, chalk, watercolour and gouache of the same name by Henry Moore)

They lie, frightened,
cocooned in their own shelter.
They try desperately to stop the noise,
hiding their heads with their arms,
six kittens pawing their faces.

No one sleeps in this shelter tonight.
They are restless, like nervous children,
worried about relatives,
dead relatives.
Though these families don't know that.

Outside they hear a fire bell,
carried through London on
the howling wind.
The dust scratches at the door.
It tries to shelter too.

The lantern hangs,
creating a dull light.
Its swaying and creaking
reminds them of the pub sign where they live.
'The Romping Donkey'.
Hardly a name to be taken seriously.
And now it's gone,
caught in last night's raid,
but living in their memories.

Suddenly the lantern burns out.
Then, a gigantic bang,
an explosion upon all explosions hits them,
like a giant puff ball,
thrown by a playing child.

Lives burn out,
like the lanterns . . .
And the all-clear sounds.

WHERE HAVE YOU BEEN?

Allison Johnson (6)

Peter Trust (14)

*A Stranger in the Dark

A man stepped out of the darkness into the little illuminated circle about our camp fire and seated himself upon a rock.

'You are not the first to explore this region,' he said gravely.

Nobody disputed what he said. He himself was proof of what he said, for he was not of our party and must have been somewhere near where we camped. We thought he must have companions not far away. It was not a place where one would be living or travelling alone. For more than a week we had seen, besides ourselves and our animals, only rattlesnakes and horned toads. In an Arizona desert people don't exist long with only such creatures as those. You must have pack animals, supplies, arms and an outfit. And you also need comrades. It was a doubt as to what manner of men this stranger's comrades might be. The presence of this stranger caused every man of our half dozen gentlemen adventurers to rise to a standing posture and lay his hand upon a weapon, expecting enough trouble from the stranger to have to lay our hands upon a weapon ready for action. The stranger took no notice of this and began to speak in the same deliberate way in which he delivered his first sentence.

'Thirty years ago, Rowell Baldwin, Campbell Bannerman, James H. Walker, and Leon Barden, all of Tucson, crossed the Santa Gatalin mountains and travelled due west. We were prospecting and it was our intention, if we found nothing, to go to the Gila river and on to a point near Big Bend, where we understood there was a settlement. We had a good outfit of men, but no guide – just Rowell Baldwin, Campbell Bannerman, James H. Walker, and Leon Barden.'

The man repeated the names slowly and distinctly, as if to fix them in our memories. Every member was now observing him closely, but were really thinking that somewhere in the darkness his companions seemed to encircle us. He seemed to be a harmless enemy. We were not new to this country but knew that the solitary life of many men in this area had a tendency to develop eccentrics and seem to be a bit mental. I had read once, 'A man is like a tree: in a forest of his fellows he will grow as straight as his generic and individual nature permits; alone in the open he yields to the deforming stresses and torsions that surround him.' I had thoughts like that as I watched the man from the shadow of my hat, pulled low to shut out the firelight. A foolish fellow no doubt, but what could he be doing here in the heart of a desert?

Having told you this story, I wish that I could describe the man's appearance. That would be the normal thing to do. Unfortunately and somewhat strangely, I find myself unable to do so with any degree of confidence. None of us could agree as to what he wore and how he looked. I tried to think of my own impressions but they eluded me.

Nobody broke the eerie silence that surrounded us so the visitor went on to say:

'This country was not then what it is now. There wasn't a ranch in the whole of the Arizona desert. There was little hunting here and there in the mountains and near the infrequent water-holes there was enough grass to keep our animals from starvation. If we should be so fortunate as to encounter no Indians we might get through. But within a week the purpose of the expedition had altered from discovery of wealth to preservation of life. We had gone too far to go back, for what was ahead of us could be no worse than what was behind, so we pushed on, riding by night to avoid Indians and the intolerable heat and concealing ourselves by day as best we could. Sometimes we exhausted our supply of wild meat and emptied our casks to the highest extreme. We were days without food or drink. Then we found a water-hole or a shallow pond in the bottom of a valley which restored our strength and sanity so that we were able to shoot some of the wild animals. Sometimes it was a bear, sometimes an antelope, a coyote, a cougar, which were all food.

'One morning as we skirted a mountain range, seeking a practical route, we were attacked by a band of Apaches who had followed our tails up a dusty path, it is not far from here. Knowing that they out-numbered us ten to one, they took none of their usual cowardly precautions, but dashed upon us at a fast gallop, firing and yelling. Fighting was out of the question. We urged our animals to gallop faster up the path round the mountain until footing for a hoof was impossible, then threw ourselves out of our saddles and ran to the chaparral on one of the slopes, abandoning our entire outfit to the enemy. But we luckily got our rifles, every man – Rowell Baldwin, Campbell Bannerman, James H. Walker, and Leon Barden.

'The savages dismounted also, and some of them ran up the path beyond the point at which we had left it, cutting off further retreat in that direction and forcing us up the side. Unfortunately the chaparral extended only a short distance up the slope, and as we came into the open ground above we took the fire of a dozen rifles. But Apaches shoot badly when in a hurry and none of us fell. Twenty yards up the slope, beyond the edge of the hillside, were vertical cliffs, in which directly in front of us there was a narrow opening. Into that we ran, finding ourselves in a cavern about as large as an ordinary room in a house. Here we were safe for a time. A single man with a repeating rifle could defend the entrance against all the Apaches in the land. But against hunger and thirst we had no defence. We still had courage, but hope was gone.

'Not one of those Indians did we see, but by the smoke and glare of their fires in the gulch we knew that by day and by night they watched with their rifles at the ready in the edge of the bush. If we drew straws not any of us would like to take three steps into the opening. For three days, watching in turn, we held out before our suffering became unbearable. It was the morning of the fourth day when Rowell Baldwin said, "Señores, I have lived without religion, and I am not acquainted with that of yours. Pardon, Señores, if I shock you but for me the time has come to beat the Apaches' game."

'He knelt upon the rock floor of the cave and pressed his pistol against his temple.

' "Madre de Dios," he said, "comes not the soul of Rowell Baldwin."

'And so he left us – Campbell Bannerman, James H. Walker, and Leon Barden.

'I was the leader, so I had to speak.

' "He was a brave man," I said. "He knew when to die, and how. It is foolish to go mad from thirst and fall by Apache bullets, or be skinned alive. Let us join Rowell Baldwin."

' "That's right," said Campbell Bannerman.

' "That is right," said James H. Walker.

'I straightened the limbs of Rowell Baldwin and put a handkerchief over his face. Then Campbell Bannerman said, "I should like to look like that in a little while."

'And James H. Walker said that he felt that way too.

' "It shall be so," I said. "The red devils will wait a week."

'Campbell Bannerman and James H. Walker knelt. I then stood before them.

' "Almighty God, our Father," said I.

' "Almighty God, our Father," said Campbell Bannerman.

' "Almighty God, our Father," said James H. Walker.

' "Forgive us our sins," said I.

' "Forgive us our sins," said they.

' "And receive our souls."

' "Amen!"

' "Amen!"

'I laid them beside Rowell and covered their faces.'

There was a quick commotion on the opposite side of the campfire. One of our party had sprung to his feet and drew his pistol. 'And you!' he shouted. 'You dare to escape and leave us? You cowardly fiend, I'll send you to join them if I hang for it.'

But with a leap of a panther the captain was upon him, grasping his wrist. 'Hold it, Sam Yountsey, don't do it.'

We were all on our feet, except for the stranger, who sat motionless and apparently inattentive. Someone seized Yountsey's other arm.

'Captain,' I said. 'There is something wrong here. This man is either a lunatic or a liar. Just a plain, everyday liar who Yountsey had no cause to kill.'

'Yes,' said the captain, 'there is something unusual. Years ago four dead bodies of white men, scalped and mutilated, were found around the mouth of the cave. They are buried there. I have seen the graves. We shall all see them tomorrow.'

The stranger rose, standing tall in the light of the dying fire, which in our attention to his story we had neglected to keep going.

'There were four,' he said. 'Rowell Baldwin, Campbell Bannerman, James H. Walker, and Leon Barden.'

With his reiterated call of the dead he walked into the darkness and we saw him no more.

At that moment one of our party, who had been on guard, strode in among us, rifle in hand and very excited.

'Captain,' he said, 'for the last half-hour three men have been standing out there on the mesa.' He pointed in the direction that the stranger went. 'I could easily see them, for the moon was shining brightly, but as they had no guns and I had them covered with mine, I thought it was their move. They have made none.'

'Go back to your post and stay till you see them again,' said the captain. 'The rest of you lie down or I'll kick you into the fire.'

As we were arranging our blankets the fiery Yountsey said, 'I beg your pardon, Captain, but who the devil are they?'

'Rowell Baldwin, Campbell Bannerman and James H. Walker.'

'But how about Leon Barden? I ought to have shot him.'

'There's no need to. You couldn't have made him any deader.'

Alexandra Peake-Tomkinson (12)

It was something . . .

It was something I couldn't quite explain
It was something that wouldn't happen again.

It was cold and lonely but beautiful and wild all the same.

The cold bit my frozen hands and chewed my fingernails
    again and again.

It was something I couldn't explain
It was something that wouldn't happen again.

I could smell the warmth flowing from him and I could smell
    his hair.

It was something I couldn't quite reach, couldn't quite touch.

It was something I couldn't quite explain
It was something that wouldn't happen again.

Hidden beneath layers of skin and bone,
A feeling, deep down, somewhere.
It was like a fragment of a song, half remembered.

Laura Adams (16)

It was something I couldn't explain
It was something that wouldn't happen again.

He tapped me on the shoulder, so that I whipped round,
   with my hair flying: sky high.

My dungarees wet and sodden at the knees from where I'd
   been kneeling under the trees.

Rough tears stung my coarse throat.

It was something I couldn't quite explain
It was something that would never happen again.

I wanted people to understand, but whatever I said and
   whatever I did, it wouldn't mean a thing.

He was transparent and strange
It wasn't cold:
but something like icy wind cut through my jumper
Something like rain pummelled my face

It was something I couldn't explain
It was something that wouldn't happen again.

I had to get home, I ran and branches cut my legs.

I punched rebelliously at the wind
but it made no difference.
Closing in on me like thick walls made of iron,
I could feel his presence surrounding me.

With a mug of hot tea on my lap, Mum said, 'Looks like
   you've seen a ghost,' and maybe I had.

Isaac Raine (11)

*The Red Gang

Polly spat out the slightly bloody froth from her mouth. Flora seemed too excited to brush *her* teeth. She was crammed into a pink nightie, with 'I am four' on it, in blue letters. Polly could remember how pleased Flora had been when it was first given to her.

They were staying at Granny's, mainly because Granny was not a light sleeper.

Polly and Flora had started off a craze, a few weeks ago, of going around wearing anoraks backwards, with the hoods over their faces. The main function of this was so you could spy on the 'Red Gang', who had their headquarters at Polly's school. Flora had invented this, so she was still rather pleased with her idea, and had worn her anorak over her face for so long, her scarred knees were almost grey, a startling contrast to her pink, gawky legs.

Michael Clear (12)

Polly had said that if they spent the night at Granny's, then they could leave the house without waking Granny up, walk to school, and spy on the 'Red Gang'.

She was gargling her Listermint, singing 'Baa, baa black-sheep'. She choked on 'Have you', and spat it out on to Flora's nightie, which stuck to Flora's legs, and went transparent. Flora threw a glass of water at Polly, and missed, hitting a bowl of bath-pearls. Polly was just thinking how she should retaliate, when Granny came in and crossly told them to go to bed.

The alarm went off at eleven, and they got out of bed, sleepy and giggling. They walked down the stairs bumping into things and muttering. They went round to the door and opened it. As soon as they were outside they felt rather frightened. Flora half-giggled. Everything was very dark. Polly was afraid of spiders as they walked up the lawn. The road was totally empty, and cold on their feet. The wind blew their nighties around. They walked along, half starting sentences, but breaking off as soon as they had begun.

Suddenly Polly said, 'I want to go home.' Her hands were clasped inside her pyjamas.

'Oh,' said Flora.

They turned round and noticed, for the first time, a white van approaching. They began to run. Then Flora tripped up on her nightie, and cut her knee. She got up limping and crying.

Michael Clear (12)

Charles Murray (12)

'Polly! Wait for me!'

Polly ran back for her, but by then the van had stopped by them. The window opened and a fat man with grizzled grey hair said, 'Like a lift?'

'*No*,' said Polly and ran away, holding hands with Flora.

Ignoring the gravel, they reached Granny's house. They ran straight across the lawn, forgetting spiders, and to the front door.

It was locked, and Granny *was* a heavy sleeper . . .

Matthew Ledgerwood (8)

The Boat Ride

Oh most of me frights and shivers
Oh and the boat on the sea, on the sea,
For me a key I'm looking for

The special key you see
He be the captain I see land
And find the key for he.

I look to the west and
The east in the ship
But no key.

A cat got in my way and
I saw a trunk but no key

Another trunk
And in the trunk
Was the key.

Archanna Ramu (8)

The Number 11

A number eleven ran away by itself,
He tore himself out of a book,
And stood up straight with perfect legs,
Sliding down pencils,
Sliding down books.
The number eleven is a happy number,
Getting more and more tired but he still ran on,
He sticks himself on so many books,
Then he jumps off a desk,
But he lands on his feet.
Climbing on a different desk,
He said,
'Oh what a good place to be.'
He lay down flat,
And stuck himself down.
A shadow came upon him,
A hand he saw with a rrrr . . .
Terrified he tried to get loose,
The rubber came more and more down.
No use, it's just no use.'
He was gone in just a click of the fingers.

Caroline Brett (11)

Sara Worts (12)

*Astronaut

He stood, gazing at the earth, dreaming of his flower
  garden . . .

Green tips of seedlings poking from the compost,
opening their leaves to be warmed by the Sun,
the Sun bouncing off the greenhouse:
tomatoes turned orange to red
and worms crawled in the damp soil, sunning their skins.
His wife planted seedlings; making a hole with her index
  finger,
she eased in the marigold.

Chris Daunt (11)

He missed catching the 7.56 to Leeds,
the click of the typewriter printing a's and e's
on the headed note-paper.
He missed the tone of the telephone
and the lift saying 'GOING UP'.
Then there were . . .

Sunny afternoons on the heath
wandering down sheep paths,
in amongst the heather.
Heather, a blaze of colour like fire,
reds and oranges.
And when he got home there would be
crumpets rich with butter,
crumpets like the moon . . .

Like the moon.

Kevin Dawson (12)

145

Lucy-Ann Dale (16)

The Key-man

The key-man came
From the bottom of the corridor,
And looked down the red –
Patterned carpet.

Saw the stand-up, spaced-out
Ashtrays. The doors,
Twelve on the right side, thirteen
On the left. White.

Shuffling, he moved up
To the first door. Opened it. Checked it.
Carefully,
Taking the keys from his overall –

Pocket and locking away the secrets
Of the last day's business. Another door
On the other side.
Checking, looking, locking.

Twelve doors on the right side, thirteen
On the left. White.
Up to the window-wall end, showing the city,
Then,

He turned shuffling
Back to light,
As only an old man can,
Counting,

Thirteen doors on the right side,
And twelve on the left. White.

Laura Moran (6)

Lucy Pyne (15)

*Passing

My buspass is my passport;
It's just ten minutes' ride,
From Brixton into Dulwich,
It is the great divide.

> No soldiers here, no checkpoints,
> No great forbidding wall,
> But manners, language, customs,
> You have to change them all.

From Palladiums to loafers,
And Chipie to Chanel,
Karan, then into Naf Naf,
From street-cred into swell.

> These kiss like Continentals
> Or shake a manly hand:
> These nod a casual greeting
> And too much talk is banned.

'Wicked', 'safe' and 'well 'ard',
Or 'fab' and 'brill' and 'great',
'Really super, darling',
Or 'it was blindin', mate'.

> I think that I'm bilingual,
> I think that I can pass;
> But I'm a tourist really,
> And I'm travelling second class.

Would I rather be a 'Ragga' or a 'Jagger'?
Would I rather be a 'Shazza' or a 'Sloane'?
I think that all this class
Is just a load of farce –
I'd really rather make it on my own.

Helena Echlin (15)

*Driving at Night on the Motorway

Iron crocuses,
Throat-lozenge orange,
The lampposts zip up the night.

And the traffic drums,
Heavy as water
Or steady bombs in the distance.

This is a therapeutic journey,
Grey sound bandaging me,
Regular as blood pounding,

And the space-invader lights
Are peaceful as if
They were on my eyelids.

There is nothing to be seen
But the nebulae of cities,
Houses which may be stars.

Katy Knight (16)

Who's to say
In the darkness
If anything else exists
But this?

Why not only the motorway
Stretching out across
The unfathomable spaces?

In the night
The lights make a kind of
Heavenly punctuation – commas, full stops,
But no words.

Candice Brett (8)

*Fred, the St Kilda Puffin

The Missing Puffin

There was a puffin called Fred. He lived on St Kilda. He was born on the cliffs. One day he was wandering around when his mother got caught by a man with a rod with a loop on the end. Fred was very sad.

He made sure he didn't go there again. One day when he was flying he fell into the sea by mistake. He tried to get out but he couldn't get out. Some thunder clouds came and the little puffin closed his eyes and went to sleep. While all this was going on the puffins were looking worriedly on. When the little puffin woke up he could see land.

Two days later the puffins were really worried. Luckily Fred got washed up on Scotland beach. A little girl came by and saw the little puffin. She picked him up and took him home. She gave him some small fish. When he could fly well she let him go. He went to the beach and flew to St Kilda his home. When all the puffins saw Fred they were very happy.

Fred and the Storm

One day Fred was on the peak of St Kilda when a storm came. He tried to fly down to shelter but he didn't have time. He almost got struck by lightning. Luckily he didn't. He hid in a rabbit's burrow.

Soon a little boy came by trying to get out of the storm. He didn't like killing animals so he picked up Fred and took him home. When he got home he made a little bed for the puffin and put him in it and then left Fred to have a little sleep. Next morning the little boy gave Fred some fish and when it had stopped raining he let him go.

He flew back where he should be at that time. He flew as fast as he could go. On the way though the storm came back and he couldn't see where he was going so he hid in the rabbit burrow again until it had stopped raining. Then he flew all the way home and told them everything that had happened for those three days.

Fred and the Ladies that Spun

One day Fred was wandering around when he saw two ladies spinning. He watched them spin for a little while then he walked away but just at that moment the two ladies saw him and they grabbed him and took him home. They put him in a room and locked him in there. He couldn't get out. All the windows were shut and so were the doors. He heard them whispering and wondered what they were saying.

Soon they came and took him out of the room and gave him some fish. Then they said that he was going to stay there until morning. That night he couldn't sleep. He thought about his friends on the cliffs. He thought of his relatives and relations. Soon morning came, the ladies came and woke Fred up and then did some spinning. He watched them and walked around.

After a while he had his breakfast. The ladies let him go and he flew all the way back to the cliffs. When he got back the first thing he did was tell everyone he was back. Then he told them the story and showed them the little scarf the ladies had spun for him.

Fred and the Millers

One day Fred was flying past some people grinding corn when a grindstone hit him in the eye. He fell to the ground and stood up very very carefully. One of the women picked up Fred, bandaged his wing and his eye and then let him go.

On the way home the bandaged wing felt much better so Fred took the bandage off. He hurried home and when he got there his wing started to bleed again. Fred walked back to the millers and the lady said, 'Let's take you home,' and she took him to her house. She gave him something to eat. Then she bandaged up his wing.

She made him a little bed and said, 'Go to sleep now,' and the little puffin fell asleep. Next morning the lady took the bandages off and then let him go. He flew all the way home and told everybody everything. Then they all said, 'Why do you get all the adventures?' and Fred told them why he got all of the adventures.

Fred and the Lifeboat

One day Fred was wandering along when he saw a lifeboat being launched. He wondered why it was being launched then he guessed that someone must be in trouble. He followed the people to see what was happening. There was a boat that was sinking and the people were drowning.

Fred stood on the edge of the boat. He watched carefully as they pulled everybody out of the water. Fred followed the boat back to the island. Then he flew all the way home. Then he got every puffin on St Kilda to the meeting place. Then he told them all about it and they said, 'Well I hope we see one of those boats one day.'

A long time ago the St Kildans only had little fishing boats and some special rods to catch puffins with. They spun with the spinning wheels they had and they wove. The people cut the wool off the sheep to make clothes.

Fred Goes to the Fair

One day Fred saw some people going to the fair. He said to himself I think I will go too. So he followed them to the fair and looked around. He saw the Merry-Go-Round. Fred had a go on it. He went on a pink horse. Then when the ride had finished Fred felt dizzy.

Then he went on the Roller Coaster. He didn't like it at all. Then he went to see what other people were doing. He saw some people playing on the swings. He saw people playing on the coconut shy. He was enjoying himself. He watched people get ice-creams. Then he had a go on the ghost train.

When the ride was finished he was very scared. Then he went home and they all said, 'Where have you been?' Fred said, 'I have been to the fair.' They stared at him. Then they all went home.

When the St Kildans Left

One day the St Kildans left St Kilda. They packed up all their belongings and then waited for a big ship to come. Soon a ship did come. They said, 'Will you take us to Scotland?' The person driving the boat said yes.

So everybody put all the parcels on the ship and off they went. Fred watched them go. He thought about all the people that had helped him. He thought about the fair he went to the other day.

Soon the ship was out of sight. Fred said to his friends, 'It's quiet, isn't it?' They all agreed. Fred stayed on St Kilda and he had loads more adventures but that's another story.

— The End —

Puffins have striped beaks. The beaks are different colours through the summer. They are pretty fat birds. They live on islands around Britain. They feed on shell-fish and small fish. The male bird digs a hole in the ground so that the female bird can lay an egg. They have white breasts and grey round the eyes. They have orangeish reddish legs and feet. They have black on their wings.

The True Story of St Kilda

A long time ago in St Kilda there lived a few people. They were very poor people. They kept some sheep. They had to cut the wool off the sheep to make clothes. They had some cats and dogs as well. They had to catch birds and fish to eat. Most of the time they caught puffins. They had some corn fields. Some of them cut the corn and others grinded it. Some of them spun and some of them wove. There were no trees or wood on the island so they got the driftwood that landed on the island. They had to rub two dry sticks together to make a fire. They had a few boats. One day some people came from other countries. The tourists told them about England and Scotland. They told them about the food they ate and the things they drank. When they left the island the St Kildans thought about what they had said. They made up their minds to go. They packed up their belongings and took their best sheep. They left the cats on the island to catch the mice but they drowned the dogs.

Rosalie Gorniak (7)

*Curly's Adventure

Chapter One

It was a watery day in a liquid world. The soaked ground was soggy. The wind was beating the trees in the wood. The rain was drumming so loudly that the trains could hardly be heard. The electricity pylons were swaying about and their cables flapping. The allotments were drenched, and the paths between the vegetable plots had become streams, racing downhill towards the river. Mr McCane was wet through, like a drowned rat. He had been caught in the cloudburst and he was drenched. His green boots slurped at every step in the mud. He was putting away his tools. His face was streaming and he wiped the drips on his nose with his wet sleeve.

Oh well. He would soon be home, warming his feet in front of the log fire, sipping a hot, sweet cup of tea and eating one of his wife's scones. He locked his shed and began to trudge the half-mile to his cottage. The rain was getting lighter now, and the wind was dropping.

By dark, the rain was a very fine drizzle. The clouds had moved on so the edge of the cloud could be seen, and beyond the edge, in the darkening sky, hung the crescent of the new moon and a solitary star.

A stillness lay over the allotments and then the compost heap, that Mr McCane had so lovingly created, came to life. Tiny creatures had woken up, because, for them, the coming of darkness was breakfast time.

The earwigs were the first to stir. They could smell the delicious marigolds that Mr McCane had just thrown on to the compost heap. Red was leading the way up through the steaming layers to the surface. Pincers was following behind, puffing in his attempts to keep up.

First they passed the two worms, Wriggle and Long, and stopped for a chat, and to invite them to breakfast, which the worms declined with a polite 'No thank you'.

Next they met the millipedes gliding along. Their names were Silver and Grey. As soon as they saw Red and Pincers, they each curled up in a tight little ball. They were very unsociable.

The earwigs carried on up to the slugs' quarters. Slime and Speedy were just waking up. They complained that the earwigs had disturbed them. They were lazy and liked to lie in late if possible. The earwigs hurried on their way, bumping into Legs and Mustard who were coming down from the same path. The centipedes were very friendly and just as busy as the earwigs, so they got on together very well.

Suddenly Pincers had to stop because Red had halted in the middle of the path.

'Why have you stopped?' he asked.

Red replied, 'The snails are on their way up and are taking up all the room, so we'll have to wait.'

Soon however, they were all on the top of the heap, breathing in the fresh night air. The two larger snails, Stalky and Glider, were sliding in a dignified way towards some old cabbage leaves, while the younger snail, Curly, was rolling and turning, and proclaiming loudly that he was doing his morning exercises. He took one look at the moon, did a backward somersault and announced that he was going on an adventure to the cabbage patch, at the far end of the allotment.

Stalky and Glider told him to stop being so foolish and to come and have his breakfast at once. Curly took no notice at all, and disappeared over the edge of the compost heap. Stalky and Glider said, 'Oh well. He'll be back sooner or later,' and they settled down to eat some nice cabbage leaves.

Chapter Two

Curly had reached the bottom of the compost heap. He was feeling elated. He was dancing a Tango and pretending a dandelion was his partner. He hardly noticed how wet the earth was, as he wound between the large puddles. The rain had stopped and the moon lit up the mountain of the compost heap that towered behind him.

'The beginning of my adventure to the end of the allotment,' he said. He gave a little jump of delight. He had made this trip many times before, but each time it gave him the same pleasure.

As he crossed the potato bed he noticed the rich smells of the onions growing ahead of him. He climbed the mound, went under the leaves of the potato plants, and then, from the top of the mound, he could see the long thin leaves of the onions, arranged neatly about six inches apart.

He carried on, dancing as he went, until he was near enough to taste a fresh young onion leaf. A little further and he was nibbling the soft green fronds of a carrot top. What a delicious feast! A meal fit for a king, that would have a final course of tender young, pale yellow, cabbage leaves. Much better than the leathery old ones on the compost heap. He went on to the parsley bed and had a taste of the green leaves. They went very well with his carrots.

Then, just as he was going around a large puddle, making his way to the leeks, he met the hedgehogs, Prickles and Snuffle. They greeted him and asked after his friends in the compost heap. Curly was very happy and explained that he was having an adventure. Prickles and Snuffle decided to join him. They passed the leeks and finally came to the cabbage patch.

Rows and rows of delicious young cabbages. Curly was thrilled. He made for the biggest and fattest cabbage of them all. He climbed up the stalk and made his way through the large leaves into the centre where the heart of the cabbage was yellow and tender, and he began to feast.

Prickles and Snuffle had been hunting beetles and they had found so many that they were now full and sleepy. They called to Curly, but they could not hear him answer, so they decided to go home.

Curly had fallen asleep with a large smile on his face, right in the middle of the large cabbage.

Chapter Three

The next day Mrs McCane asked Mr McCane if he would go to the allotment and bring her some potatoes and two of the largest cabbages. She was running out of vegetables. And a little parsley would be nice, she thought. So Mr McCane put on his green boots and walked down to the allotments with his bucket and his knife.

When he got there he stood back and admired his neat

rows of vegetables. The rain yesterday would do them the world of good. He pulled up six beautiful large potatoes, knocked off all the mud and threw them in his bucket. Then he went to the cabbages, and chose the two largest. He cut them and put them on top of his potatoes. Finally, he cut some sprigs of parsley, and gently squeezed them into a space between the cabbages in his bucket. Then he set off home to his dear wife.

Curly woke up feeling rather ill from eating too much. His head felt giddy as though he was swinging from side to side. He climbed slowly to the outside of the cabbage and found in horror that he was being carried in a bucket by Mr McCane.

What was he going to do? He went back into the middle of the cabbage, to think. Suddenly the motion stopped and all was quiet. Curly waited for a bit, and then nervously he poked his head outside the cabbage and had a look around.

He was still in the bucket, and the bucket was outside Mr McCane's back door. No one was in sight. He quickly slid out of the cabbage and down the outside of the bucket. He hurried along the edge of the wall to a cardboard box, which he hid behind. From here he looked around and saw that he was in a garden with many coloured flowers. The tidy beds surrounded a lawn, and in the middle of the lawn was, horror of horrors, a bird table. Curly did not like birds. He moved back behind the box and found a little hole. Entering, he discovered that the box was upside-down and empty. It would make a safe place to hide in.

He was feeling rather scared and wishing he had never come on this adventure. He felt lonely and missed his friends in the compost heap. He cried himself to sleep.

Chapter Four

When Curly woke, it was night and he decided to explore the garden and look for some food. He made his way along the edge of the flowerbeds. He drank some rainwater from a fallen leaf and felt much better. He passed some rose bushes, marigolds, sunflowers, and some sweet-smelling shrubs. Not a snail in sight. He carried on to the bottom of the garden where there was a hedge. Half-way along this, he heard a faint rustling sound. Turning around, he saw two brown mice.

'What are you doing here?' they asked crossly. 'Snails are forbidden in this part of the land. In fact, Mr McCane put snail poison down in these flowerbeds.'

Curly explained what had happened.

'Well you'd better go back then,' the mice said, unsympathetically. Curly told them he didn't know the way, and the mice ran off, complaining that he was stupid.

Curly miserably carried on round the garden being very careful not to eat anything.

As he was nearing the end of the last flowerbed, which brought him back to the house, he saw a dark shape lying on the path. He went to investigate. It was a blackbird. Curly stepped back again. He was scared of blackbirds. As he watched, the blackbird opened his eyes and saw Curly.

'Please help me,' he said. 'The cat has hurt my wing and I will die if I don't get help.'

'Promise you won't eat me,' said Curly.

'I promise,' said the blackbird.

'Can you move?' asked Curly.

'A little,' replied the bird.

'Then you can come to my box,' said Curly.

He led the way slowly and the blackbird pulled himself along the path until, finally, they reached the box.

The bird squeezed in through the hole behind Curly.

'Please could you get me some water?' asked the bird panting.

Curly agreed to try. He found in the nearest flowerbed some fallen pink rose petals filled with rainwater. One by one, he took them to the bird until he had refreshed himself.

'Is your wing broken?' Curly asked.

'No, just badly wounded,' the bird replied.

Curly knew that marigold petals were good for healing wounds. Glider had taught him that. So he fetched ten petals and laid them over the wound. The blackbird tucked his head under his good wing and went to sleep.

Chapter Five

Two days later, Curly was looking much thinner as he had only had water and no food. The blackbird was better and his wing hardly hurt at all. Because of Curly's care, he had recovered. He felt very grateful and asked how he could repay Curly.

'I only want to go home,' Curly said mournfully, 'but I don't know where it is.'

'Tell me about it,' said the blackbird. 'I may know the way.'

'There is a railway line going over a river, and some tall metal pylons which hold up wires. And there is a wood where tall trees bend in the wind. The compost heap near the potato bed is my home. It is the neatest garden where there are rows and rows of gardens growing vegetables, but there are no houses.'

The blackbird thought for a moment and then said, 'The allotments, that's where you live. I will take you there on my back.'

So, when dark fell, the blackbird let Curly climb up on to his back and he took off high up above the garden. He soared over the cottages and very soon Curly could see the electricity pylons. Their route followed these giant towers until the bird flew lower, saying, 'Here are the allotments. Which one is your home?'

Curly peered down, but none looked familiar. Then he saw one that was weed-free and tidy, with rows of sweet cabbages and a compost heap at the other end.

'There it is!' he cried. 'That one there, with the shed.'

Chapter Six

Curly's friends had missed him. His excitement and playfulness added such joy to their lives. Without him, the allotment was quiet and felt empty.

After the second night had passed, still no Curly, they had decided that he must have been eaten by a bird, and they had wept for him. Stalky and Glider had felt very bad about letting him wander off on his own.

They were comforting each other on the top of the compost heap and suddenly noticed above them a blackbird was coming down to land. They quickly hid under a cabbage leaf, hoping they would not be eaten. Then, to their surprise, they heard Curly's voice saying, 'Thank you, blackbird, for bringing me home. And be careful of the cat.'

The blackbird said, 'It's thanks to you, Curly, that I am alive. I will never forget you saved my life, and if ever you need help, call me.'

With that he flew away.

Glider and Stalky came out from under the cabbage leaf. Curly was so pleased to see them that they all hugged each other and cried tears of joy. Curly vowed never again to go on adventures. The first thing he wanted was a meal from the cabbage leaves on top of the compost heap. He would never again visit the cabbage patch at the far end of the allotment. At least, till the next time.

Amy Sanderson (6)

Peter Dawson (5)

*I Went Dancing

I went to dancing class and I liked it. I liked the witch one best. It was feeling like that we were real witches. My bones were moving me and the lady was playing on the piano. Me and Joel liked it. We did tap with our tap shoes on. The tapping was going right through my legs.

Lara Pearce (6)

Jennifer Dashwood-Evans (8)

Peter

Tool

Hannah Webster (6)

165

IN TIME TO THE RIPPLES OF THE EARTH

Scott Burkeman (14)

Evan Brown (10)

The Intruder

My foot, an active part of my body,
Doing something so innocently proper
Heel, toe; heel, toe.
But yet I feel a hatred for this movement
Stirring the Sycamore leaves,
Breaking their logical peacefulness.

The destructive foot of man
Breaking through nature's skeleton,
To me, a symbol
Of what man has done
On a much bigger scale
To all the races of our earth –

Every step I take,
A mechanical intrusion.

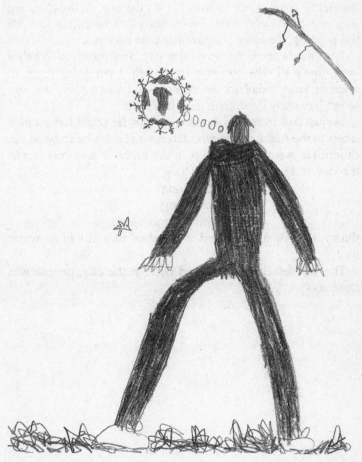

Calum Brown (8)

Jojo O'Neill (6)

*The Story of the Crying Sun

Once upon a time there lives a crying sun. Nobody knows why the sun is crying maybe it is the people? The smell of the fields? No it is not all that. No it's the city. In the morning they are loud noisy cars, buses, lorrys, farmer's tractors, all the pipping, flashing of lights that hurt his eyes.

The sun wanted to leave the city and move to another land, that's all. The sun said to himself, I am going to go to another land today in the night. But I can't, then the city won't have any light, then they can't see.

He just had to stay in the city. At least he could have a nice sleep in the night. So he wondered what it is like to be in the desert! He went to the desert in the night. It was very hot in the desert. He walked a very long
long long
long long
way he was very
thirsty. He saw a little pond. He dashed to it. It had no water in it.

The sun fell down dead and back in the city, people was dead too.

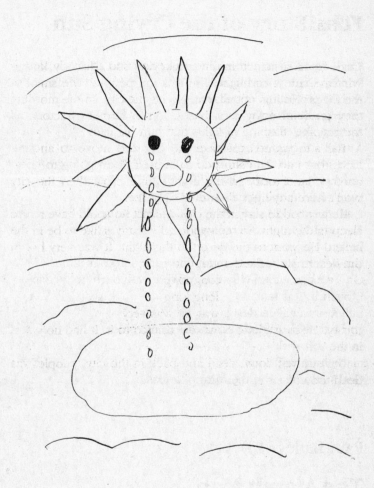

Jojo O'Neill (6)

171

Jessica Brown (12)

Fossil

Small detail sustained in time, right down to a fish's scales,
Printed shadow and light.
A shell protecting its treasure,
never to be broken.
A stone skeleton.
A snail a thousand ages old,
bailed out into the cold rock . . .
Hard prints of a once lived life,
Light filtering the mind's eye
Until the world's shape is moulded into stone.
Corrugated iron, rock, cobweb?
Ridged-ribbed-rock.
Grooves engraved into mud, into rock, into our minds.
Or a wax-moulded chrysalis, waved, wax burnt to a crisp.
I touch it. It is taut,
pulled into naked design
and left to be folded and kneaded into shape
In the soft rock –
made into hard rock.
God's artwork is in the form of a fossil.

Paul Batley (13)

The Marsh Man

He lay under the bed of reeds
at Oak Field Marsh,
protected by peat.

Until one day an archaeologist,
who was digging for bones,
stumbled across this human dinosaur,

held together by the thinnest of threads.
Like the shadows of two
skyscrapers

touching tips together
but never colliding.

Oh no, never colliding
until the thread snaps
and then he's truly
dead in our minds.
Forever.

Until, one day,
we dig again.

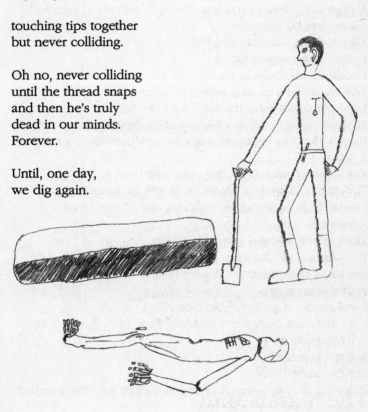

Nick Block (11)

Fiona Shackleton (16)

Bloke-Oak

Bloke-Oak, I am, that is my name.
Old, I am,
My mother threw a seed into the earth and the ripples still
ring around my trunk.
I do not see, but hear and feel.
Pictures are painted for me.
I suckle from the sun,
The wind that trips and barely breathes upon my leaves
Can sometimes paint for me a wild law-lacking canvas.
My skin is furrowed and I know all in these woods.
I know the rosy light that drips through the clouds onto the
grass.
The pungent stink from the garlic plant.
The rustles, scratches, snatches, chirpings, squealings,
warblings, howlings, munchings, crunchings of the
animals.
Their hearts tick and I can hear them.
But most of all I love the plants; they are my kin.
See them now, closed and snug for the night, drowning in
their own aroma.
I feel my heart grow echoes now,
I could almost burst for wondering how each flower is so
transcendent.
See the snowdrop.
See the snow drop.
Dripping over the stem, freezing at the last possible moment
before a drop of water plips.

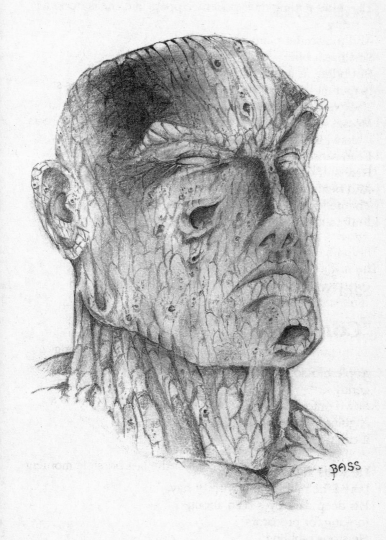

Guy Bass (16)

The bluebells
Ringing delicate smells all over the grasses.
The wind rattling their pollen-clappers like shells upon a
  string.
And the scarlet pimpernel.
Small as a pin
But bright as a comet.
Forget-me-not; the sun and sky glow from its petals.
The perfect summer's day, hidden among the shrubs.
Mosses and ferns cover the ground beneath me and insects
  crawl in my lofts.
I can sense the time clocks beating,
Hearts of different planes.
And behind the chiming wood,
The neddy-steady thump of Bloke-Oak's heart,
In time to the ripples of the earth.

Sara Worts (12)

*Conker

Apple blossom blows,
gently
down onto the hutch.
A guinea watches from the wire;
it can't be snow!

He waits at the wire;
bored, he nibbles at a wisp of hay.
His deep dark eyes scan about,
looking for predators.
He stops nibbling.

A noise.
He heard something.
He turns and runs into the undergrowth,
and camouflages himself.
An army recruit in battle.

The scuffle has ruffled his hair.
He has rosettes on his back;
it is as if someone
has blown on his hair,
hair which is soft to touch,
yet looks coarse,
like the Timothy grass that grows by the back door.

And while I feed him,
Chestnut peeps out from under the hay
as the blossom blows.

Kim Pearce (12)

James Mitchell (10)

Wind in the Trees

The wind blew.
It wandered and whistled
Looking for a tune,
Trying the notes in the leaves,
Singing secret scales.

The wind lifted the twigs
Like a conductor,
And the trees bent to the baton.
The grass bowed
Across a thousand strings,
Every blade pulling in unity
and singing the same song.

A beating of drums,
Rain rattled on leaves,
Music lifted in gusts
And trees raised their branches
In a fanfare of trumpets.

Voices of a choir
Faded and fell.
The trees bowed
To a final gesture.
Birds rose in a flutter of applause.

James Mitchell (10)

Martin Berry (8)

The Hyacinth

The bulb is swollen with food spherical and rounded. Red as wine. The skin is thin as paper, rustling in my hand as I hold it. Roots white as snow. Trapped in a glass prison. Wrapped around each other. Vertical as a ruler as they draw up the water. Leaves upright like a blade on a knife. Buds clustered together to protect the flower when it is in a bud. Bell shaped flowers ringing silently, their smell filling the room.

Emma Walkey (13)

*Snapdragon

A frilled lip of gold, of gold dust falling from sunshine,
The puckered mouth of the silently angry dragon,
Wavering up on his green stalk tail,
Waiting.
Curl of scarlet velvet, his fire scorching the dust,
Licking the wall in a cluster of flames.
In cockerel comb splendour, the plump cushion
Is heavy. And the delicate neck is wrapped in wax paper
For protection.
A splash of rippling flag and he is crowned with gold
    fringing,
Triumphant but brooding.
He is a cavalier's doffed hat, flamboyant feather
Picked out in gold.

Barnaby Love (11)

Battle colours charge the wind on a beige charger of lace,
His jousting pole, a beam of piercing sunlight,
Pretending to be jolly.
But the flushed skirt of rage does not fool anyone . . .
The tight collar strangling the light,
And the false smile, weatherbeaten into his lips.
The stem is strong green raffia,
But elastic, stretching further than it should,
So that when you pinch, he lurches to bite,
Clamping sour lips on flesh.
But the crusty dragon, old and lemon lipped
Cannot harm.
He has little perfume.
That which he has is stolen from the rose and dried.
In winter, he shrinks back
With rheumatism, his one master, the wind.
But always back in the summer.
A bumble bee, sensing blossoming danger,
Buzzes near and far.
The hum mingles with the hiss,
Of wind on earth and leaves.
The hiss of the dragon.

Eleanor Borer (10)

181

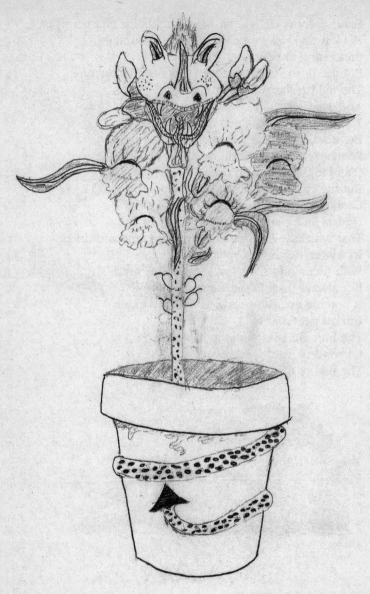

Marilyn Rust (13)

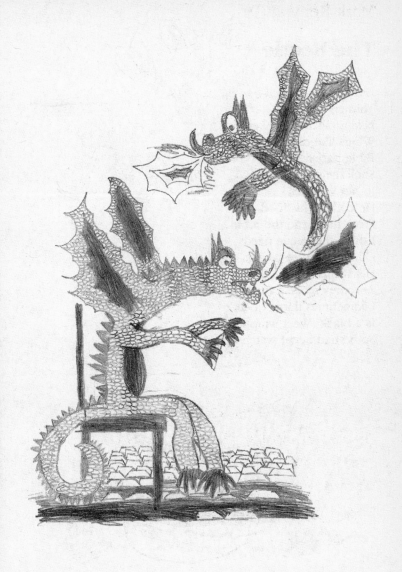

Christopher Busby (11)

Mark Kenyon (9)

The Beetle

Hard, smooth shell
Thin crispy legs
Like a piece of broken ruler.
Wings like old torn piece of
Bible paper,
Shell feels greasy
In hot weather.
He collects his food
From his friend the robin.
I think the beetle needs
Oiling, because its legs creak.
His wings are all thin,
And they make a funny noise.
I sometimes think a beetle
Is a black sweet wrapper,
So he had better watch out.

Mark Kenyon (9)

Colin Andrews (8)

Snail

Under the stone in the garden
        there is a snail.
        With a smooth delicate shell,
        protecting him from his predator
        the thrush.
Soft moist body
        fixed permanently to his black, brown
          and yellow shell.

Silently
        on his moist foot
        Slowly crawling over the dewed grass
        he meanders
        leaving a trail of silver as he goes.
Tentacles, like wire
        turning
        helping him with the never-ending
        hunt for food.

Sarah Ralston (6)

A Rabbit

I will call him Snowy
He will be white
A black ring round his right eye.
He'll jump.
He'll run.
He'll sit down and go to sleep
Floppy ears
Like white, soft feathers.
A twitching nose.
Little sharp claws. Please.
I want a rabbit.

Rebecca Seery (9)

Sebastian Carter (7)

Anne Mason (8)

Caroline Cane (7)

THE PICTURE HANGS THERE TALKING TO SOMEONE

James Clarke (10)

Adrian Alderson (8)

The Picture

The picture hangs there talking to someone.

It hangs on the wall watching every move of the person.

It hangs on the wall staring at the person.

But the person just ignores it.

Katie Bowman (10)

Joanna Smith (8)

Tom Cutting (9)

Seema Motala (9)

Simon Fraser (10)

To Make a Horse

When you're out looking for a horse, you should
go out exploring.
When you find one you find a tree to hide behind.
Then carefully draw the fences round the field.
Paint the grass and the water box.
Draw the head.
Then two eyes and nostrils.
Then do the ears and the mane.
Add the tail so you can see it is several little pieces.
Then put the body on
Leaving four spaces for his legs.
If you hear a bird singing you know you have made
a good picture.
The horse will now allow you to stroke it.

Marcus Isaacs (9)

*To Paint a Penguin

Paint a picture of icy water with a
Flat low cliff and carefully paint a
Penguin on the cliff.
Paint a sunset in the distance and
Paint a sun going in behind the clouds.
Then the penguin waddles to the edge
Of the cliff, and jumps into the water,
Head first.
It has caught a fish.
Now it's eating it.
Then paint the dark, black sky with stars
In it, and a big moon shining in the night.
The penguin goes into his cove and
Goes to sleep.
But first the penguin dips his foot
Into the ink and puts his inky foot
In the snow in the corner of the
Painting.
It is the penguin signing his
Signature.

Marcus Isaacs (9)

Gemma White (12)

Ennui

(From the painting of the same name by Walter Richard Sickert)

A case of stuffed birds imprisoned by glass,
Flecks of colours that the artist has captured.
An old woman stands in the corner of her kitchen.
Gazing at them,
She is also trapped,
But by the finest of brushes and the thinnest of paint.
Her husband,
Slumped in an old wicker chair,
Stains the air with his cigar.
Remembering . . . when he was young,
and the birds he trapped.

He wants them all to be free.

Gemma Brown (12)

Calum Brown (8)

*From My School

The rustle of leaves from naked trees
The skeleton of a sycamore towering above
I close my eyes.
My red eyelids feel the warm,
Welcoming rays of a cool sun.
A breeze brushes against my face.

The ferry floating,
Muffled voices.
White foam splitting the bay.
The pier looking lonely and bare,
Arms reaching into the sea.
A winding road.

A little boat leaves the pier
Like a baby after its mother:
Its mother gently glides round the point
Leaving it helpless, slowly moving.

Birds, a blanket of white silk
Covering the beach,
Calling . . . Waiting . . .
All this in one corner of the Atlantic.

Roisin Starrs (8)

*The School Playground

In the school playground it is usually quiet. When it is, it is like a deserted island, with the trees swishing gently in the soft calm wind. The walls are heated by the warmth of the hidden sun. From a distance you can see tall mountains and far off houses up up in the sky. They are all so high. It is like heaven when the playground is empty.

But . . . when the bell rings the children put on their coats and then it's . . . PLAYTIME! The playground is no longer a deserted island. Now all the fun and games begin. Everyone plays games like Polo, Red Rover, Tig Relay, Jack Frost and lots more. Everyone's having a good time. The trees begin to shake and the birds all fly away because they are frightened of the children who want to play. We all wear the same clothes so it is difficult to tell where your friends are. If I am lonely I love to look out at the beautiful view of houses and mountains far away. I love to do that. But I think the hospital spoils it, because nobody likes the hospital. Sometimes the postman comes, he says,

'Hello, boys!'

We laugh and carry on with our games. Sometimes we talk about good times and things to do with my friends. In the summer we lie down and watch the grass being blown about by the gentle breeze, and then stare up at the few fluffy white clouds and the blue patches scattered about the sky. It is a beautiful sight to see. I like the playground while it is quiet and empty because it is like heaven then.

Una Garvey (9)

Christopher Royston (8)

The Adelphi Hotel (1870–1990)

Once there was light coming from the windows.

Now there is glass shattered.

Bricks broken scattered around.

A rusty chair.

Two forgotten walls staring at nothing.

by Tim Ellis.

Timothy Ellis (8)

Rachel Armstrong (16)

**Unattended Café

Waiting for the waitress
the child could have seen
the melted butter smeared on the plastic counter,
the flies buzzing over the damp, hot sugar,
the greying aprons hung from rusty hooks
and the mug of scummy water
in which they kept the scoop warm.
But instead
he saw the swallow's nest in the raftered ceiling.
And he watched his cracked flip-flop scuff the floor
as he tried to remember the French
for
chocolate ice cream.

Rosamund Bird (12)

Elizabeth 1st

There she sits on her perch,
Isolated from the world.
Like the eagle,
High, mighty, cold and harsh.
Her eyes bleeding
Anger, sadness and loneliness
She makes herself like a doll:
Look but don't touch.

She has pearls instead of children,
Bows for love,
Rubies for kindness.
She is longing for love,
But she is loveless.
She is longing for mercy,
But is merciless.

China Moo-Young (14)

Michelle De Voy (7)

*Tasty Food for Romans

Snails slither down my throat
Fattened on milk,
Roast goat.
Dormice stuffed with tasty herbs,
Delicious oysters
Swallowed whole
Bread rolls in a bowl.

Karen Spendier (10)

Roast ham and pheasant fine
Mulsum, honey mixed with wine
Dainty pastries, also dates,
These are tasty from our plates.
If I lived in Roman time,
These would be
Favourite foods of mine.

Emma Knight (10)

Peter Dawson (5)

*Brownie Slipped

I went to a harvest
and gave them some cooking apples
And I liked the harvest
because I pinched a nut
I liked the roof because
it was colourful like sky
I liked it because they
showed a big banana and some cats
and a Brownie slipped on the banana pretending
I fluttered my paper
I put it on my head and floated off
And so did Katie next to me.

School Prize Winners

The following is a list of the schools which submitted work of the most consistent merit to the Competition.

Abingdon School, Abingdon, Oxfordshire
All Saints Middle School, Sudbury, Suffolk
Avenue Infant School, Leicester, Leicestershire
Belsize Young Writers, London NW3
Bignold Middle School, Norwich
Bishop of Llandaff High School, Llandaff, Cardiff
Bishops CE Primary School, Newquay, Cornwall
Burnham Grammar School, Burnham, Buckinghamshire
Cumnor House School, Danehill, West Sussex
Dowdales School, Dalton in Furness, Cumbria
Halesworth Middle School, Halesworth, Suffolk
James Allen's Girls' School, East Dulwich Grove, London SE22
John Kyrle High School, Ross-on-Wye, Hereford
King's School, Canterbury, Kent
Lincewood Junior School, Basildon, Essex
Margaret Beaufort Middle School, Riseley, Bedfordshire
Mount St Catherine's Primary School, Armagh, N. Ireland
Nativity School, Sittingbourne, Kent
Newcastle Under Lyme School, Newcastle, Staffordshire
Notting Hill and Ealing High School, London W13
Royal Grammar School, Newcastle-upon-Tyne
Sedgefield County School, Stockton-on-Tees
Sholing Girls' School, Sholing, Southampton
Sompting Abbotts School, Sompting, West Sussex
St Patrick's Primary School, Armagh, N. Ireland
Tendring High School, Thorpe-le-Soken, Essex
Trinity Catholic High School, Woodford Green, Essex
University College Senior School, London NW3
University College Junior School, London NW3
Upton-by-Chester County High School, Cheshire

INDEX

*   Award Winners
**   Special Award Winners
   Illustrators

All Pan books are available at your local bookshop or newsagent, or can be ordered direct from the publisher. Indicate the number of copies required and fill in the form below.

Send to: **CS Department, Pan Books Ltd., P.O. Box 40, Basingstoke, Hants. RG21 2YT.**

or phone: 0256 469551 (Ansaphone), quoting title, author and Credit Card number.

Please enclose a remittance* to the value of the cover price plus: 60p for the first book plus 30p per copy for each additional book ordered to a maximum charge of £2.40 to cover postage and packing.

*Payment may be made in sterling by UK personal cheque, postal order, sterling draft or international money order, made payable to Pan Books Ltd.

Alternatively by Barclaycard/Access:

Card No.

Signature:

Applicable only in the UK and Republic of Ireland.

While every effort is made to keep prices low, it is sometimes necessary to increase prices at short notice. Pan Books reserve the right to show on covers and charge new retail prices which may differ from those advertised in the text or elsewhere.

NAME AND ADDRESS IN BLOCK LETTERS PLEASE:

....

Name————————————————————————————

Address————————————————————————————

————————————————————————————————

————————————————————————————————

————————————————————————————————

3/87